THE AMERICAN PEOPLE

The
American People
The Findings of the 1970 Census

E. J. KAHN, JR.

WEYBRIGHT AND TALLEY
New York

Weybright and Talley
750 Third Avenue
New York, N.Y. 10017

Portions of this book appeared,
in somewhat different form,
in The New Yorker.

Library of Congress Catalogue Card Number: 73–84073.
Manufactured in the United States of America.
ISBN: 0–679–40003–6
Designed by Jacques Chazaud

Author's Note

☆　☆　☆　☆　☆　☆

This book is an attempt to depict the American people as they exist in fact and not in fancy, written not by a sociologist or a statistician, but by a journalist—a "mere" journalist, a sociologist or statistician might say, and perhaps not without justification. It is based chiefly on the voluminous data compiled and conveyed by the Bureau of the Census. For assistance in foraging amateurishly through their huge field of expertise, I am enormously grateful to the many largely anonymous men and women now or until just recently in that agency, without whose patient guidance the task would have been unimaginable and probably impossible. Among those to whom I should like to express my thanks, and my apologies for conceivably inadvertent mishandling of their complex work, are Tobie Bressler, Charles Brinkman, George Hay Brown, John J. Casserly, Don Church, Alex Findlay, Paul C. Glick, Louis Greenberg, Stanley Greene, Aaron Jasowitz, Charles Johnson, Nathan Krevor, Beulah Land, Daniel B. Levine, Nampeo D. R. McKenney, Arthur E. Mielke,

[v]

AUTHOR'S NOTE

Herman P. Miller, Henry D. Sheldon, Jacob S. Siegel, Henry H. Smith, Conrad Taeuber, Joseph Waksberg, Robert Warren, Murray Weitzman, Dorothy Whitson, Arno Winard, Arthur F. Young, and Meyer Zitter.

New York, N.Y.   —E.J.K.
June 1, 1973

Contents

☆ ☆ ☆ ☆ ☆ ☆

CONTENTS

THE AMERICAN PEOPLE

I

☆ ☆ ☆ ☆ ☆ ☆

The Figure Factory

The United States of America, as portrayed by the 1970 Census and related surveys of the Bureau that conducted it, is a real land of make-believe, the most typical of whose more than 200 million inhabitants may not exist. For instance, about 20 percent of all Americans, consistent with their historical restlessness and adventurousness, change their residence every year. That is impressive, but—inasmuch as by the same token 80 percent of them stay put—it is also illustrative of the old saw that many facts can be viewed two ways: the glass is half full or half empty; at sunrise, day starts or night ends. Should we be proud that over 99 percent of our citizens are literate, or should we be mortified that, after more than 100 years of devotion to universal public education, close to a million are still illiterate?

In the twentieth century, there have been four major migratory flows within America—South to North, rural to urban, metropolitan to suburban, and just about everywhere else to California. Thus, anyone seeking to equate statistical generalities with particular human experience might conclude that the logical end product of all this shuttling about would be a poor black Mississippi farmer transplanted to a ranch house on the outskirts of Los Angeles.

But there may be no such specific person, though his existence is statistically quite plausible. For the Census tells us, among myriad other facts, that between 1965 and 1970 there was a migration of 898 individuals—conceivably at least one of them a black farmer—from the most impoverished section of Mississippi to the beckoning environs of southern California. At the same time, 191 individuals, for reasons best known to themselves (since the Census never asks for "why's" but merely "who's" and "what's"), took the same long route in the opposite direction.

Who among us has not heard in elementary school (99 percent of Americans now go to school) that the United States is a melting pot—more accurately, in modern terms, the sort of bland, drab mixture that usually results from putting into an electric blender components quite dissimilar in color, texture, shape, and taste? In fact, America is, rather, a *pot au feu* or bouillabaisse, with varied ingredients bobbing about in it more or less compatibly, but also quite individualistically. What national homogeneity we possess is surely to be found less in our people than in our highways, our airports, our motels, our shopping centers, and our garish strips that herald the imminence of a reasonably civilized settlement.

But if one takes a Howard Johnson's restaurant as

the paradigm of American sameness (and in truth the HoJo crowd does look alike wherever it convenes), one will still find differences. In some parts of the country, there might be a scattering of black tourists, but the serving staff would be all white. This would have nothing to do with personnel hiring policies but would merely reflect the circumstance that in much of America the resident black population, to which so many grubby jobs accrue, is minuscule.

The center of population of the United States, when the decennial census was taken in April 1970, lay in a soybean field 5.3 miles east–southeast of Mascoutah, Illinois, a town not far from St. Louis. The telltale spot is 26.9 miles west and 9.4 miles south of a farm outside Centralia, Illinois, which was accorded the pivotal honor in 1960.

The *geographical* center of the country has remained fixed ever since it took a giant leap northwestward after Alaska and Hawaii joined the Union. This spot has been pinpointed by the Bureau at the conjunction of Wyoming, Montana, and South Dakota; and again the site has little in common with the nation that theoretically radiates out from it. One hundred and forty-odd million Americans, for example, lived in 1970 in what the Bureau has since 1950 called Standard Metropolitan Statistical Areas (S.M.S.A.s)—that is, residential clusters consisting of a metropolitan area surrounding one or more core cities with a population of at least 50,000. There were 243 of these at the time of the 1970 Census; within two years, twenty-one more had been acknowledged

—five in Florida alone, where the palm tree is waging a game but losing fight against the traffic light.

How inappropriate, then, for this tristate rural intersection to be portrayed as the center of anything involving such an overwhelmingly urban majority! For Wyoming is one of the only three states—Vermont and Alaska are the others—that cannot, for better or worse, boast a single S.M.S.A.; and South Dakota and Montana between them can produce only three. So here we have an inland dot officially designated the territorial hub of a country most of whose inhabitants have emphatically demonstrated that, the traditional lure of the wide open spaces notwithstanding, they prefer the seacoasts; and that, moreover, three quarters of them want to live huddled together on a scant one and a half percent of their spacious land.

The typical American family, unsurprisingly, not only is not to be found at either of America's statistical crossroads but, as derived from the averaging of the known data about all Americans, is also an illusion. There may be somewhere a typical white Irish-American bus driver's family, or a typical smalltown hardware store proprietor's family, or a typical retired Iowa farmer's family, or a typical black ghetto welfare family. The Census Bureau—which has long been looking at everything and everybody quite literally in terms of black and white, and, in the last few years, also in terms of whether they are of Spanish-speaking origin—has in fact produced its version of the average all-inclusive black family of 1970: a husband of forty-one, a wife nearly thirty-nine, and three children, the oldest not quite eighteen. The parents finished their junior year of high school. They occupied rented quarters in the center of a large city, and their income was $6,280 a year. The husband had a full-time job as a mechanic, truck driver, or waiter.

The typical *American* family also could be synthesized by putting everybody into a blender—not quite nine parts white, a little over one part black, add a pinch of Spanish-speaking, a dash of Oriental, and a smidgen of American Indian. Out came a blend that could be analyzed as a white man forty-four years old, his wife of forty-one (each had 12.2 years of education), and their 2.35 children. They had access to 1.25 cars, owned 96 percent of a television set, and their principal residence (they also had a little less than one tenth of a second home) was a house of 5.3 rooms, worth about $17,000, in the suburbs of a metropolitan area. *Their* annual income was $9,867. But of course they didn't exist, because they couldn't exist; as soon as one assigned to the average suburbanite the average American income, he at once became atypical, since he couldn't live where he did on what he made.

No Americans are more sensitive to the risks of averaging tangibles and coming up with intangibles than are the individuals who spend much of their time doing just that—the 4,600 full-time employees of the Bureau of the Census. A lot of their fellow Americans tend to be cynical about census-taking, if not downright antagonistic; perhaps they associate it with distasteful memories of attendance-taking in school. Yet, in a country relentlessly engaged in self-examination and self-evaluation, the Bureau occupies a unique and lofty perch: It is the largest, the most comprehensive, and all in all the most reliable accumulator, disseminator, and, occasionally, interpreter of hard facts about the entire body politic. There are other federal agencies—the Internal Revenue Service, for example—that make it their business to seek out a great many Americans; but the Census Bureau is the *only* arm of the federal government whose operations touch (at least in theory) the life of every single person physically present in the United States at a given moment of history.

Officials of the Bureau sometimes describe themselves as "searchers for truth" and the premises they occupy as, less elegantly, a "figure factory." The Bureau has a data-processing center at Jeffersonville, Indiana, and regional offices scattered around the country; but its administrative headquarters and principal manufacturing plant are in a complex of squat, austere buildings at Suitland, Maryland, built during the Second World War. Nine miles south of its immediate superior, the Social and Economic Statistics Administration of the Department of Commerce, but somewhat off the beaten federal track, the Bureau is a relatively isolated enclave, with its own totems and its own jargon, including the casual, everyday use of words like "cohort." It even has its own apposite slogans, like "We can't know where we're going if we don't know where we are."

Information, though, does not always guarantee insight. In the 1940 Census, for instance, the population of the country was put at 131,669,275. Three years later, the Bureau announced confidently that, with birth rates declining and immigration unlikely to be of any great future consequence, the nation's head count would reach its ultimate peak in 1980, at 153,000,000. That figure was passed in 1951.

The usually knowledgeable Bureau of the Census is greatly appreciated by the sovereign states, which are sometimes unreceptive to activity generated in Washington, D.C. The reason for the Bureau's popularity is that, beginning in 1790, Census data have been gathered and published on a state-by-state basis. This readily enables the states, at no direct cost, to have a better idea than they otherwise might of where they are and where they're going. Even so, the Bureau is limited in the kinds of information it can furnish them; everything it looks into is supposed to be of national interest.

Not that all the states are always fond of the Census. It is probably safe to assume that Alabama was not enchanted by a federal judge's ruling, in 1971, that its Department of Public Safety should start to recruit blacks and continue until they constituted 25 percent of this police force. The judge took that proportion because, according to the 1970 population breakdown by states, there were 903,467 blacks in Alabama—26.2 percent of the population. By a bit more than 1 percent, the judge was giving the white supremacists a break.

The following year, the headquarters of the National Guard, in Washington, advised its offshoot in North Dakota that, because the 1970 Census had fixed the black population of that state at 2,494, the Guard there, in the interests of racial balance, should recruit twenty black members. This proved to be a problem. On examining the state's black population, the Adjutant General of North Dakota ascertained that 2,350 of the blacks already had military connections; they and their dependents were attached to an Air Force base. Of the remaining 144, more than sixty were women, who couldn't be of much help inasmuch as there were no WAC detachments in the Guard out there. Among the fifty-odd black males of military age—over eighteen and under forty-five—more than thirty appeared to have been already recruited: They were black athletes in predominantly white colleges. That left only some twenty black males in the state who could even be approached to join up. Eventually, Washington relented and trimmed North Dakota's quota to a still-hard-to-fill ten.

Meanwhile, California, which has a sizable black population, was trying manfully to transform *its* National Guard into an organization at least 7 percent black. An intensive recruiting program did result in the doubling of the blacks in the ranks, but even so their total representation rose only to 4.24 percent. The most successful recruiting area was the Watts ghetto of Los Angeles, where the then nearly all-white Guard had been summoned to try to maintain order during the 1965 riots. The new black recruits seemed to be giving credence to the old military adage: If you can't lick 'em, join 'em.

On the whole, the sovereign states find the Bureau's disclosures useful. The answers to a question like "How did you travel to work last week?," while primarily intended for the Department of Transportation, are, when furnished for each state, likely to be of considerable benefit to its highway and public works agencies, not to mention to its proprietors of filling stations and pizza parlors. Moreover, the Bureau further refines its findings and issues them by counties, by metropolitan areas, by urban tracts (small metropolitan areas, each with a population of about 4,000), by (in Louisiana) parishes, and even by city blocks—a million and a half of these for 1970—thus enabling a local housing official or school board or welfare administrator to know with fair certainty, say, just how many school-age children from Spanish-speaking families with incomes below the official poverty level there are in any given locality.

Such information, coupled with data on the number of families headed by a woman alone, may affect the choice of the site of a neighborhood day-care center. Or—since Census figures are also much scrutinized by businessmen, large and small—they may make it possible for an olive wholesaler to determine in what parts of a city he is most likely to find supermarkets that cater to substantial numbers of people with origins in Greece.

From the outset, however, the main responsibility of the Census Bureau has been to provide the federal government, once each ten years, with an accurate nationwide head count. Census Day is April first of every year that ends in a zero, and by December first of that year the Director of the Bureau is supposed to let the President know exactly how many people he presided over eight months earlier. The White House was duly informed on December 1, 1970, that the magic number was 203,211,926—177,748,975 whites, 22,580,289 blacks, and 2,882,662 "Others."

The figures change minute by minute, of course, and, while the Bureau can undertake to make complete head counts only every ten years, it does put out periodic estimates of population increases. It was confident that the 210,000,000 milestone would be passed, by chance, on Election Day in 1972; and its estimators calculated with far greater precision that, on the stroke of midnight as 1973 got under way, the total would have reached 210,194,312.

That figure was sharply adjusted in a subsequent estimate; early in 1973, the Bureau reported that the turn-of-the-year population had been merely 209,717,000, and that the population increase in 1972 of roughly 1,628,000 had been the lowest annual numerical gain in any year since 1945. In terms of the national growth rate—the 1,628,000 coming to 7.8 new persons for each thousand old ones—1972 had ranked lower than any year since 1937, which had scored no better than 6.7 per thousand.

But even more important than the overall population in 1970 was the breakdown by states, for these figures are the ones that, since 1929, have determined the apportionment—and, if necessary, reapportionment—of seats in the House of Representatives. In 1910, when Arizona and New Mexico were approaching statehood and—there being nothing of the continental United States left—the makeup of the Union seemed forever fixed, Congress set the number of Representatives at 435. This averaged out to a more or less manageable quota of 210,583 per legislator, though of course with a minimum of one person per state and with Nevada, for instance, then having a total population of only 81,875, there were disparities.

Then along came Alaska and Hawaii, and the number was raised to 437. But Congress evidently felt uncomfortable with that untraditional membership, and in 1960 it reverted to 435. This meant that a couple of states had to lose Representatives; but that is what usually happens anyway after each decennial reckoning. These gains and losses provoke anxieties and even outcries in state capitals; when it appeared in 1960 that Massachusetts would have been first in line for a four hundred and thirty-*sixth* seat, had any such been authorized, that state tried vainly to get Congress to raise the total again.

After the 1970 Census, Congressional district boundaries were redrawn in no less than forty states. The only ones unaffected by population shifts and by a Supreme Court decision about fair representation were Hawaii, Maine, Nebraska, and New Mexico— each a state with only two or three districts, and thus not cartographically complicated. The other six states were too small to be divided into districts at all; each has a representative at large.

California, whose population had increased by 27 percent since 1960, was the big winner in this odd game of chance. It picked up five additional seats. Florida got a raise of three. The principal losers were New York and Pennsylvania, which were stripped of two seats each—a sharp blow to the pride of the once dominant northeast. Oklahoma edged out Oregon for the crucial four hundred and thirty-fifth seat; some people not familiar with the rules of the game thought this was a question of alphabetical order, but it was simply statistical good fortune.

Some Congressmen, who are supposed to be their constituents' personal liaison men with the federal establishment, do not regard it as good fortune of any sort that, with the population rising every year, they turned out after the 1970 Census to have constituencies averaging 465,000 apiece—more than twice the dimensions of the body politic for which each of their counterparts was responsible in 1910. One factor that swelled the constituencies was that in the 1970 Census, for the first time ever, the 1,580,998 Ameri-

cans living abroad on April first—businessmen, servicemen, and other government employees and their
families—were credited to whatever state they chose
to designate as home.

All in all, the current distribution of Congressional
seats seems remarkably fair; in 371 of the 429 existing
districts, the 1970 population ranged narrowly between 450,000 and 500,000. Until 1980, when the
cards in this particular deck are reshuffled, the
Congressman with the smallest constituency will be
from Alaska (total apportionment population in
1970, including 1,894 expatriates: 304,067), and the
one with the largest from North Dakota—which, with
a total population, including 6,420 expatriates, of
624,181, had not yet quite reached the level of South
Dakota: 673,247, and barely in the two-representa-
tive category. Nevada remained a one-man, one-vote-
in-the-House state, but, whereas its Congressman in
1960 had spoken for only 285,000 voices, a decade
later that chorus had swollen to 492,396 (including
3,658 distant voices)—which was a larger number of
people than any of neighboring California's forty-
three Representatives could claim for his very own.

For all the understandable interest each state has
in harboring the largest number of individuals who
can be voted on behalf of, the Census Bureau has
discerned, in regular surveys it has been making since
1962, a persistent condition of apathy among the
individuals who are entitled to do the basic voting. In
Western Europe, in Canada, and in Australia, between 75 and 95 percent of eligible voters faithfully

exercise their franchise. The practice in the United States has been dismayingly different. In the 1970 Congressional elections, characteristically, only 55 percent of all Americans who could have voted bothered to do so. And the Bureau's researches have further revealed intimations of aberrant behavior that have hardly reflected credit on the world's self-proclaimed preeminent democracy. There has emerged from every survey a high number of individuals who profess not to be able to remember whether they voted on the previous Election Day.

There are even more people who for one reason or another—perhaps guilt is a principal one—insist to enumerators that they have voted though, when their collective assertions are matched against the total votes cast, they manifestly could not have. A generation ago, 6 percent of the voting-age population fibbed about going to the polls. In 1970, the number of apparent dissemblers rose to 13 percent, which may have meant that Americans were feeling guiltier than ever about not participating in the elective process.

In 1971, the Twenty-sixth Amendment to the Constitution was ratified, and the national voting age lowered to eighteen. That seemed to be a wholesome, generous gesture on the part of the Congress toward younger people, who had been protesting on nearly every campus that the reins of government were too tightly and conservatively held in middle-aged or elderly hands. Yet there had been no statistical evidence that youth—even that segment of youth to which there were real or imaginary differences between political parties and candidates—cared much about exercising *its* rights of franchise.

In the 1970 Congressional elections, by which time a few states already permitted eighteen-year-olds to vote, the highest proportion of voters—65.2 percent —had been in the forty-five- to sixty-four-year age group. The lowest proportion—25.7 percent—was in the eighteen- to twenty-year group. In absolute terms, there were more voters over sixty-five than there were under thirty. The potential new voters, it was widely thought when the Twenty-sixth Amendment passed, were biding their time, waiting for their first appearance at the polls that really mattered—the 1972 Presidential contest. The thinking was not unanimous. The political scientist Seymour Martin Lipset, for instance, pointed out that the broadening of enfranchisement did not necessarily have a liberalizing effect on the nation's destiny. Lipset was reminded that, after the passage of the *Nineteenth* Amendment in 1920, which enfranchised women, Warren G. Harding got the largest majority any Republican candidate had ever had.

On Election Day in 1972, the Bureau estimated that there would be 25,000,000 Americans under twenty-five eligible to vote (11,000,000 of these between eighteen and twenty), and that they would represent 18 percent of the entire population of voting age. They could, accordingly, have had a sharp impact on the shape of things political, but to do so they would have had to depart sharply from the lackluster performance of their peers in the 1968 Presidential election. That time, barely half the eligible voters under twenty-five had voted; nearly three quarters of those over twenty-five had.

The hopes of Senator George McGovern and his staff hinged in large part on how the 25,000,000 would perform. Those Democrats who predicted victory did so in the expectation that 75 percent of the young group would vote and that 75 percent of *them* would vote for McGovern. Of course, nothing of the sort happened. Only 55 percent of the whole electorate went to the polls—the lowest percentage in a Presidential election since 1948—and the youngest group did even worse, only 48.3 percent of the eighteen- to twenty-one-year-olds claiming to have voted and as many as 41.9 percent of them not even taking the trouble to register to vote. Among these younger people, the men made a slightly poorer showing than the women. By abstaining, they at once created a statistical generation gap, for two thirds of the over-twenty-five group did vote, and the forty-five- to sixty-four-year-olds claimed a 71 percent turnout—they may have been exaggerating a bit—and thus managed to wield influence disproportionate to their numbers.

If Senator McGovern's partisans were surprised, the Bureau of the Census was not. Its crystal-ball experts, who are chary about making predictions but will cheerfully put forth estimates, had guessed well ahead of Election Day that, even with so many possible new young voters around, the median age of all Americans who went to the polls on Election Day in November 1972 would be a quite mature forty-three. The actual median age turned out to be 44.9.

II

☆ ☆ ☆ ☆ ☆ ☆

All in the Line of Inquiry

Between decennial summations—during what it calls its intercensal periods—the Census Bureau compiles reports not only on voting but on a large number of facets of American life. There are regular studies of housing construction starts and department-store inventories, of freight-loading and city-government finances. In every year that ends with a "2" or a "7," the Bureau conducts a massive Census of Transportation; in the "4" and "9" years, a Census of Agriculture; in the "3" and "8" years, an Economic Census. (During the "1," "5," and "6" years, it pauses gratefully to catch its breath.) Data for the last Economic Census were provided, early in 1973, by 2,100,000 representative businesses, big and little, that responded to Census questionnaires, and that did not enjoy the privilege of begging off; corporations, like individuals, are required by law to cooperate with the Census. The data thus gleaned will by 1975 or thereabouts be disclosed, broken down by manufacturing, mining, transportation, service trades, wholesale trade, and retail trade.

On a narrower level, there will be summaries of the activities of engineering companies, travel agencies, and architectural and law firms. In a vastly more constricted area of inquiry, the Bureau gamely keeps up with, and churns out statistics about—to cite just a tiny fraction of its categories—green coffee, dried food, residential demolitions, ice, macaroni, corn products, nonwoven felts, both broadwoven and narrow fabrics, cooperage, cut stone, leather tanning, pens and pencils, brooms and brushes, Venetian blinds, nonregulated bus and truck carriers, and pickles.

Much of what the Bureau learns is later disclosed by other federal agencies. Under whatever auspices government statistics may be released, 98 percent of them originate with the Bureau of the Census. The Bureau is the primary collector, for example, of the raw material from which the Bureau of Labor Statistics prepares its monthly revelations of unemployment rates. When the Cost of Living Council wanted a quick survey made, late in 1971, of how the first phase of President Nixon's wage–price freeze program was working out, it called upon the Census Bureau; there was no other agency around with the resources and skills to tackle the job.

But the biggest job of all remains The Census, and it has become a big one indeed. The results of the first United States Census, conducted in 1790 under the aegis of Secretary of State Thomas Jefferson, were issued in a single volume fifty-six pages long; the entire operation cost $44,000—1.1¢ per person counted. The price tag for the 1970 Census has been calculated at $247,653,000, or $1.22 per capita. Its output is taking two forms, microfiche tapes and printed pages—more than 200,000 of the latter alone, in some fifteen thousand separate publications. To be sure, most of the work is now done by computers. The Bureau of the Census blazed a trail in 1951 when it committed some of the processing of its 1950 survey to the mercies of Univac I, the first nonexperimental use of a computer by any organization anywhere.

Since then, the Bureau has relied increasingly on computers. Today it uses a clever contraption called a Film Optical Sensing Device for Input to Computers—"FOSDIC" for short—which can magically ingest raw data, smoothly digest them, and transmit them to a computer to be further refined and printed up, all this without a single human hand's clumsy intervention. Even with computers, however, it is unlikely that the total output of the 1970 Census will be ready for perusal until the 1980 Census has begun. The final publication based upon the *1960* Census, the weighty and invaluable monograph "People of the United States in the 20th Century"—written by Irene B. Taeuber and her husband, Conrad Taeuber, he until recently the Bureau's guiding demographer— was not released until December 1971.

The 1790 Census was strictly a head-count affair and contained only five questions, including one that was dropped as superfluous in 1870; each house-holder had been asked at the start how many slaves he owned. Negroes were then, at least proportion-ately, a more significant element in the total popula-tion than they are today; the overall 1790 population of 3,900,000 (only 5 percent of it west of the Appalachians) was almost 20 percent black. If that census was skimpy, it did establish a precedent, and one that the Founding Fathers had considered so consequential that they had embodied the taking of a decennial population count in the Constitution.

Scarcely ever had a nation so young made such a commitment. There had been many censuses of one sort or another in the past, of course; in ancient times, it was important for rulers to know how many able-bodied males were around to wear their armor. Even while the earliest settlers were gingerly explor-ing America, attempts had been made by what authorities there were to count noses and, presuma-bly, guns. In 1650, there were supposed to be 50,000 non-Indians in the American colonies (nobody totted up the Indians; it was troubling enough to suspect there was one behind every tree). A century after that, on the eve of the Revolution, the total *non*-In-dian population of the thirteen colonies was put by the best-informed authorities at 1,200,000.

While the United States was precocious, among emerging nations, about taking a census, it was laggard, however, in establishing a permanent bu-reaucracy to handle the task. This chore could hardly be expected to have a high priority on the agenda of the State Department, and in 1830 the responsibility was transferred to Interior. It was not until 1902, though, that the Congress set up a full-time bureau, which it put administratively under the Department of Commerce and Labor; when this was split up in 1913, Commerce got the Bureau, and has had it ever since.

The Congress might have dragged its feet even longer but for the public relations acumen of the then-director, William Rush Merriam. As A. Ross Eckler, a latter-day director, tells the story in his "Bureau of the Census,"

> A letter that Dr. Walter F. Willcox [chief statistician of the 1900 Census], then ninety-nine years old, wrote to Morris Hansen [then the Bureau's assistant director for statistical standards] on August 6, 1959, includes an entertaining explanation of the reason for a permanent bureau: "Director William R. Merriam handled Congress very cleverly; got a stunning group of girls on his staff, nearly all of them, no doubt, wanted to remain in Washington, and in the Census Office (at least until they got married). These girls, I was told, brought so much pressure on Congress that . . . the office was made permanent, not for any scientific reason, but to keep the staff from being disbanded."

Article I, Section 2, of the Constitution, which prescribed the census as a national institution, had enjoined the Congress merely to count the "free persons" within its jurisdiction. Over the years, the undertaking grew increasingly inquisitive and elaborate. James Madison, for instance, thought it would be useful, for military recruitment purposes, to determine the number of young men sixteen and over. The first time anybody was asked where he or she was born was in 1850. In 1880, enumerators inquired about idiots and the various supposed causes of their plight.

The largest number of questions asked of anybody in the 1970 Census was seventy, but four fifths of the people enumerated had to respond to no more than twenty. These included a handful of hard-core facts about personal characteristics: The number of living quarters at each address and the number of people in each household, the name of each person and his or her relationship to the head of the household; and, for each individual, his date of birth, sex, marital status, and color or race (white, "Negro or black," American Indian, Japanese, Chinese, Filipino, Hawaiian, Korean, or "Other").

The remaining questions asked of all respondents had to do with housing—the number of rooms per residence, for instance, the value of owned establishments or monthly cost of rented ones; the number of rooms in both, and the availability of kitchen facilities, piped water (hot and cold), flush toilet, bathtub or shower, and telephone; and whether the living quarters under scrutiny had their own entrance or had to be approached through someone else's—this

[28]

last still another demonstration of the concern of the national administration in 1970 for personal privacy.

Eighty years earlier, in 1890, the acme of curiosity had been reached. There were so many questions and questions deriving from questions that there was a theoretical possibility of eliciting 13,161 responses from a single individual. There were so-called supplemental schedules for the Indian population; for persons who had died that year; for the insane, the feeble-minded, and the idiotic; and for inmates of benevolent institutions and soldiers' homes. *Everybody* was supposed to be asked for

Address; number of families in house; number of persons in house; number of persons in family; name; whether a soldier, sailor, or marine during Civil War (Union or Confederate) or widow of such person; relationship to family head; race; sex; age; marital status; whether married during census year; for women, number of children born and number now living; birthplace of person and parents; if foreign born, number of years in the U.S., whether naturalized or whether naturalization papers had been taken out; profession, trade, or occupation; months unemployed during year; school attendance; literacy; whether able to speak English, and if not, language or dialect spoken; whether suffering from acute or chronic disease, with name of disease and length of time afflicted; whether defective in mind, sight, hearing, or speech, or whether crippled, maimed, or deformed, with name of defect; whether a prisoner, convict, homeless child, or pauper; home owned or rented and, if owned, whether mortgaged; if family head a farmer, whether farm rented or owned and, if owned, whether mortgaged.

Subsequent to that, however, other agencies were in a position to provide the government with the information it needed about idiots, dialects, and deformities; and, moreover, the Congress, which has always been extremely watchful of its census-takers, made certain inhibiting stipulations about their activities. In 1902, for instance, when the Bureau was institutionalized, Congress instructed it to find out about religious affiliations (as well as urban social conditions and crimes, these last conceivably added because the legislators still had a strong rural orientation); but by 1946 it was felt that religion was too sensitive a matter to pry into, and Congress forbade any further prospecting in that lode.

Between 1850 and 1936, however, the pre- and post-Bureau canvassers had been asking church organizations the size of their memberships. Even though the estimates that emerged were probably generous, the upshot was that only about half the population seemed to be affiliated with any formal religious institution. Inasmuch as that could have been interpreted to indicate that the other half set little store by organized religion, the government of a nation that was forever invoking the blessings of God didn't go out of its way to publicize the findings.

More recently, church groups conducting their own surveys have come up with a total of 128 million members. The last time that the Bureau itself looked into religion was 1957, when it checked up on 35,000 sample households. The individual approach produced a quite different result: Only 5 percent of those questioned said they had no religion. Whatever church affiliations they had presumably were casual.

One disclosure of this survey was that Protestants and Catholics had just about the same fertility rate. The reason was that black people and rural people tended to have more children than white people and urban people: Most Catholics were urban, and most rural folk were Protestant. In fertility, actually, Catholics lagged well behind Baptists, one third of whom were black. Projecting its figures to cover the country as a whole, the Bureau arrived at a religious profile that demographers suspect still pretty much holds true. The United States is 66 percent Protestant, 26 percent Catholic, and 3 percent Jewish.

In 1940, a whole new area of investigation opened up when the first national Census of Housing was conducted; President Franklin Roosevelt had declared the nation to be one third ill-housed, and ever since the Bureau has been studying this residential malaise. Questions have been eliminated, too, from time to time, because they appeared to elicit more confusion than clarification. In 1960, enumerators were instructed to describe the condition of the homes they visited as "good," "dilapidated," or "deteriorating," but this practice was abandoned when it developed that less than half of the appraisers could agree on the meaning of "dilapidated."

The earliest enumerators, in 1790, were 650 United States marshals and their deputies. By 1960, there were almost exactly 190,000 additional ones—hired, as decennial census-takers regularly are, on the recommendation of members of Congress from the political party occupying the White House. In 1970, there were only 160,000 of these workers; 41,200,000 households were asked to provide information about themselves by mail, and, somewhat surprisingly, 87 percent of those approached docilely filled in and returned their forms.

The number of enumerators had changed radically in 180 years, but the contemporary ones bear certain similarities to their forerunners; they often get the same uncordial reception. Toward the end of the eighteenth century, census-takers—their status as marshals notwithstanding—were sometimes horse-whipped or thrown into horse troughs. Toward the end of the twentieth, some were taken into court and charged with invasion of privacy.

In point of fact, since 1880 all Census data on individuals have by federal law been confidential. The Bureau may not tell anything about an individual to any other federal agency, let alone to an outsider. After Pearl Harbor, when government authorities were rounding up persons of Japanese

descent in California and confining them in intern-
ment camps, the Bureau was asked for a list of all the
names it had of individuals of Japanese origin. The
Bureau refused.

The only exception to the rule is made for people
who have no birth certificate but need proof of birth
to obtain, say, a passport, or Medicare coverage. If
these individuals let the Bureau know when and
where they were born, it can provide them, for a
five-dollar fee, with an appropriate document. (This
takes four to six weeks. For *six* dollars, one can get
high priority, two-week service.) The Bureau does
this for several hundred thousand persons a year
through something called a Personal Census Service
Branch, at Pittsburg, Kansas—one of a number of
sideline operations in which the Bureau is engaged.

Another, known as the International Statistical
Program, conducts courses on demographic and
related subjects for foreigners; it also sends advisers
abroad at the request of nations hopeful of establishing censuses of their own. In 1972, five such Census
Bureau advisers—wholly civilian, wholly nonmili-
tary—were stationed in South Vietnam.

However often the Bureau tries to reassure the
public that when it comes to information about any
individual its files are sacrosanct, suspiciousness
persists—both among the poor, afraid that something
they divulge may get them in trouble with the welfare
authorities; and among the rich, afraid of the Internal
Revenue Service. In an era of credibility gaps, it is
little short of impossible to convince people that what

one arm of the federal apparatus knows another cannot even peek at. One man may believe that what the Bureau elicits from him the F.B.I. or the income-tax agents can never see, but another may be harder to persuade, especially if he lives in an urban ghetto where nosiness is one of the few forms of behavior that is generally accepted as a crime. One of the most astounding, and heartening, facts to be gleaned from the 1970 Census was that in the taking of it nobody was known to have died in the line of duty.

In the line of inquiry, there have been many other changes as the country has changed. As recently as 1930, children ten years old were considered fair game, and indeed necessary game, for Census enumerators seeking to paint an honest picture of employment. At the turn of the century, one quarter of all male Americans between ten and fifteen were by Census criteria—if not perhaps by their youthful own—"gainfully employed"; and thirty years later 6.4 percent of them still were. But now, statistically, child labor has blessedly ceased to be a matter of national concern; while the 1960 Census inquired about workers as young as fourteen, the 1970 enumerators did not believe there were enough of them still around under sixteen to ask about.

Other circumstances have resulted in the abandonment of other lines of inquiry. Until recently, as a component of the decennial housing survey that now accounts for thirty of the Bureau's seventy questions, the government was curious to know how many families had radios. But now it assumes that every family has at least one radio and merely inquires about battery-powered models: the civil-defense authorities, needing something to do, want to know what means they have of communication should an enemy attack knock out electricity. There are no more questions about electricity itself; there remain of course some installations that even during peacetime lack it, but in this neon nation its availability is no longer a matter of statistical consequence.

Conversely, television was not even a subject of inquiry until 1950. By 1970, however, the medium had become so prevalent that the Bureau had already begun to consider dropping it from consideration. By then, 95.5 percent of the housing units in the United States had television, and the proportion would probably have been even closer to 100 percent if every residential nook and cranny was within receiving range of some transmitter. Whereas, for instance, 99.2 percent of occupied farms in Rhode Island had television, only 89.8 percent of those in the Western mountain states did, and in Alaska, with perhaps the highest proportion anywhere of isolated domiciles, the figure was a mere 43.6 percent.

The universality of television can be indicated in many ways. Of the nation's 68,000,000 occupied housing units, to cite just one example, 2,850,000 were without complete kitchen facilities, which might be considered essential for the enjoyment of American life above the subsistence level; almost exactly the same number were without television. There were more residences lacking either a bathtub or a shower than there were lacking television. There were nearly three times the number lacking telephones than those lacking television. What is more, over 18,000,000 American households—28.7 percent of the total—had two or more television sets; only 28.2 percent had any kind of washing machine.

The national dependency on television blankets the economic spectrum. While only 1.1 percent of rural blacks in Mississippi, the poorest of the poor, had dishwashers (it was perhaps surprising that any did), 85.9 percent of them had at least one television set. Over 40 percent of all American housing units in 1970 had *color* television, and even 16 percent of those occupied by families with incomes under $3,000—substantially beneath the poverty level—had these. Households with incomes under $5,000—that was, 32.5 percent of all households—owned 26.1 percent of all the television sets extant and 15.8 percent of all the color sets.

Statistically, the United States is epitomized by three great homogenizing forces: television, public elementary education, and the automobile. When on the eve of the 1960 Census the Bureau let it be known that it proposed inquiring about motor vehicles, the automotive industry at once drew up ten questions that it thought might be helpful to have answered. Whereas the Bureau believed that it might be worthwhile, on behalf of the government's highway and traffic-control experts, to inquire about where cars were to be found, it was of no mind to conduct a marketing survey on behalf of Detroit.

Accordingly, it asked just one question, and this was not so much to learn whether people owned cars as whether they had access to them. We shall discuss this at greater length in a later chapter; for the moment, suffice to say that a similar question in the 1970 Census revealed that 80 percent of all Americans, whatever their sex, color, geographical location, financial standing, or educational attainment, had the opportunity to get into a car and go somewhere—and, if they should all have elected to avail themselves of the opportunity at the same time, to create a traffic jam of fantastic proportions.

The full list of seventy questions was not asked in 1970 of all the nation's households (there were in addition 5,786,363 individuals who at census time were living in institutions like prisons, colleges, nursing homes, and mental hospitals), but in some instances of a 15 percent sample and in others of a 5 percent sample. (Five percent of anything does not sound like much, but it represents ten million Americans.) But there are vast areas of information that are not covered by the Census. Among subjects that would normally be regarded as of considerable general interest that the Census does *not* explore are union membership, stock ownership, smoking, life insurance coverage, taxes, and the national per capita exposure, by decibel–hour, to electronic musical instruments.

Even within the areas that it *does* investigate, the Bureau's research is limited in depth, and some of its own employees have lately been arguing that perhaps they should be spending less of their time on routine quantitative measurements and more of it on psychographics—that is, trying to ascertain not merely how many people there are and whether or not they have a dishwasher, but also why they behave as they do. But to get too profoundly into areas involving abstractions and value judgments is something that an agency dependent on a firm and fickle Congress must approach with considerable circumspection. Never from 1790 on, accordingly, have any of the millions of enumerators who have asked billions of questions of their fellow Americans been officially authorized to ask a single one of them if he is happy.

III

☆ ☆ ☆ ☆ ☆ ☆

Stand Up and Be Counted—
Or Undercounted

THE DECENNIAL CENSUS IS BASICALLY A MIDDLE-class tool, wielded by middle-class artisans, who by experience and training do not as a rule go around searching for communes in caves. They are not ideally equipped for tracking down dropouts and hideouts, although they do try valiantly to account for every American and have special programs designed to ensnare transients in hotels, motels, and tourist camps, and even derelicts in flophouses or on park benches. In the main, though, they assume that Americans live in reasonably conventional households—as the overwhelming majority of Americans, of course, do—and that if they are called on persistently enough they will sooner or later answer their doorbells. But there are a lot of Americans now who will not respond to such a summons, or who in fact do not have a doorbell or a door, so there is bound to be in any count of heads an undercount.

There always has been—ever since the marshals rode into the Appalachian hills in 1790 to count, or try to count, their apprehensive inhabitants, even then inhospitable to prying outsiders, however virtuous the nature of their business. Recently, the Census people have had some of their time-honored methods challenged. Middle-class as they are (and people who deal in averages could hardly be anything else), they still tend to assume that in every household of related individuals there is one who can be singled out as the head of the household, and that if the household includes an adult male he is *ipso facto* the person.

Such hypotheses, though, are not now universally embraced in those portions of society where all old-fashioned authority figures are suspect. Delegations of women have appeared at Suitland to suggest that a married woman living with her husband deserves some categorization other than that which the Bureau's rigid terminology now forces upon her: the wife of the head of a household. And, when it comes to that, liberated individuals of both sexes are becoming increasingly resentful of the Bureau's inability to think of a coresidential couple as coequal man and woman, rather than dominant husband and appendant wife.

But as things stand to date the Census has no way—statistically—of coping with couples other than to consider them a husband with an attached wife. Is it possible, too, that when the 1980 Census comes along homosexuals will be resisting enumeration because the Bureau only recognizes heterosexuality? Hidebound though the Bureau may to some skeptics seem to be, it regards itself as an agency trying valiantly, within the limitations of its bailiwick, to keep up with—even get ahead of—the frenzied times. Not only was it a pioneer in the use of computers, but in the mid-1940s it experimented boldly with sampling techniques, then in their relative infancy. How radical a proposition, by Census Bureau criteria, that was! For the whole *raison d'être* of the Census had been not to base any findings on sampling, but to beat the bushes and get a count on *everybody*, literally, body by body. In 1937, though, there had been a sobering revelation. Toward the end of the Depression, the federal government had undertaken a nationwide mail survey of unemployment, and in a routine check of its accuracy the Bureau had done a sampling of 2 percent of all postal routes. To the consternation of all concerned, the spot check was acclaimed (after still more esoteric checking) as more accurate than the original poll.

Not long afterward, the Bureau came around to thinking that, to get a clear picture of the big picture, sampling was the answer. In taking censuses of businesses, for instance, it was agreed that those that were the most difficult to enumerate and that took the most time, trouble, and expense to ferret out were the very ones it mattered the least to know about— the marginal businesses of little or no import to the country at large. According to Joseph Waksberg, one of the Bureau's leading sampling methodologists, refinements in sampling techniques have made complete censuses unnecessary for the nation as a whole, and even for large subdivisions of the nation.

In demographic circles, that sort of talk, a couple of generations ago, would not only have been revolutionary; it would have been heretical. Like many of his associates at the Bureau, Waksberg is a man who deals obsessively with facts and has few illusions about them. In a 1969 paper on changes in census methods written with Leon Pritzker, Waksberg declared, "Much of the census history of the past twenty-five years has been a history of discovery of how inaccurate the counts of population have been, and how difficult the problems of counting are."

While the general public is sometimes surprised to hear that Census figures are not beyond question, this is no news to the nation's enumerators themselves. They are among the few bureaucrats in any federal establishment who have consistently and candidly and voluntarily conceded that they make mistakes. They make them all the time—though not for lack of trying not to—and for a variety of reasons. The Bureau's first reckoning of gainful farm workers in 1920—especially among women and children tilling the fields—was implausibly dissimilar from its findings in that limited area ten years before. It turned out that the 1910 Census had been taken on April fifteenth, when practically every pair of hands available to a farmer was being put to use; but that the 1920 Census had been taken on January first, when a good many farm families were in a state of virtual hibernation.

Our census-takers were first reminded of their

probably inescapable fallibility in 1790, by George Washington, who declared,

> Returns of the Census have already been made from several of the States and a tolerably just estimate has been formed now in others, by which it appears that we shall hardly reach four millions; but one thing is certain: our *real* numbers will exceed, greatly, the official returns of them; because the religious scruples of some would not allow them to give in their lists; the fears of others that it was intended as the foundation of a tax induced them to conceal or diminished theirs; and thro' the indolence of the people, and the negligence of many of the Officers, numbers are omitted.*

For every superintendent of a Census like the 1860 one who asserted, "It is evident that the population in all varieties of young and old, male and female, was a present and visible fact to the enumerator, with scarce a chance of omission," † there has been another like the 1870 one who—at a time when the taking of the Census was spread over several months —countered with,

> More of the error inevitably enters, through the inadequacy of the provisions of the existing

---

* *The Writings of George Washington*, ed. John C. Fitzpatrick (Washington, D.C.: U.S. Government Printing Office, 1939) 31:329.

† Census Office, *Population of the United States in 1860*, Eighth Census, 1860, pp. iii and xlii.

census law, than is pleasant to contemplate . . . a *de facto* enumeration is of course impossible. . . . When it is considered how many thousands of persons in every large city, how many tens of thousands in a city like New York, not only live in boarding-houses, but change their boarding-houses at every freak of fancy or disgust, not to speak of those who leave under the stress of impecuniosity and therefore are not likely to leave their future address or advertise their residence, it will be seen how utterly unfitted is such a system of enumeration to the social conditions of the country at the present time.*

Following the 1900 Census, the Bureau took the somewhat arrogant view that its figures just had to be regarded as irreproachable: "The population . . . was 76,303,387. A careful census is like a decision by a court of last resort—there is no higher or equal authority to which to appeal. Hence there is no trustworthy means of determining the degree of error to which a census count of population is exposed, or the accuracy with which any particular census is taken. . . ." †

By 1950, though, the Bureau was resigned to its own imperfections, and began conducting regular self-analyses that it called Post-Enumeration Surveys.

---

* Census Office, *The Statistics of the Population of the United States*, Ninth Census, 1870, 1:xxi-xxii.

† Census Office, *Special Reports: Supplementary Analysis and Derivative Tables*, Twelfth Census, 1900, p. 16.

By 1970, it was so determined to corroborate its own
accuracy that its budget for that decennial count
included $3 million for self-evaluation alone—just
about the same amount that it had cost a century
earlier to take the whole census. Among the Bureau's
ways of going about this were to compare its figures
on births and deaths with those accumulated by the
Public Health Service. All births and deaths are
required by law to be reported; although there seems
to be some doubt about how meticulous the report-
ing is on deaths, Census Bureau investigators have
satisfied themselves that less than 1 percent of all
American births go unregistered. Thus they can take
birth records, adjust these for the recognized percentages of infant deaths, compare the net result with the
population figures they have for individuals under ten
born since the last decennial Census, and see what
discrepancies remain.

Even then there are caveats. As Pritzker put it in
still another relevant collaboration, this one with N.
D. Rothwell,

In 1940 a match of the Census results with birth
records indicated considerable underenumera-
tion of infants. The presumption was that people
did not think of their infants as household
members or, if they did, it was in some special
most-easily-forgotten category. In 1950 a similar
match was performed but follow-up inquiries
revealed that 80 percent of the times when
babies were missed their parents were also.

Hence, the problem was not, as originally thought, underreporting of infants *per se* but missing of entire families in which infants were present.*

Specialists in the rarefied field of demographic analysis have more or less indisputably determined from historical precedents, however, that more boys are born than girls, and that the sexes don't balance out in the total population (women later forge triumphantly ahead) until the age of eighteen. When in any given area, therefore, the Bureau scrutinizes any given age group and perceives that instead of there being, say, 98.6 men of thirty-five for every hundred women of that age, there seem to be only 87.2, it can reasonably conclude that something has gone wrong.

After the 1970 Census, accordingly, the Bureau at first suspected, though it could not prove, that it had probably undercounted the population by 5,700,000 people, or 3.1 percent of the total. (It later revised its guess and decided it was short by perhaps 5,300,000, or 2.5 percent.) It used various methods of self-evaluation to arrive at its conclusions; it compared some of its findings about individuals over sixty-five with appropriate Medicare records, and it compared its figures on low-income black males in the District of

---

* Leon Pritzker and N. D. Rothwell, "Procedural Difficulties in Taking Past Censuses in Predominantly Negro, Puerto Rican, and Mexican Areas," paper prepared for Conference on Social Statistics and the City, June, 1967, p. 16.

Columbia with motor vehicle bureau records of the issuance of drivers' licenses. Such are the mysteries of large-scale enumeration, though, that even while confessing to the likelihood of its having missed a good many people, at the same time, examining its own performance, the Bureau suspected that it might actually have overcounted its undercount.

A dramatic and sometimes traumatic after-effect of the 1970 Census was the attention focused on its findings by municipal officials. The reason was simple enough. When the Congress enacted revenue-sharing legislation in 1972, it stipulated that direct federal grants to cities, towns, and villages be based on the recipients' population according to the most recent decennial census. This provision soon provoked demands by some communities that national censuses be conducted at intervals more frequent than every ten years; for to give a rapidly growing place so and so much per capita in 1978, say, on the basis of a 1970 head count could be manifestly unfair. The new town of Columbia, Maryland, for instance, had 8,815 residents in 1970, and expected to have many more by 1980. In 1960, it hadn't existed, which meant that if there had been a distribution of funds in 1969, it would have received not a cent.

To insure a somewhat fairer distribution of shared revenues, and for other high-level reasons, the administration decided early in 1973 that in 1975 it would inaugurate a mid-decade survey of the country. Congress approved it, though it has traditionally resisted a full-blown Census every five years; someone might get notions about redistricting the House of Representatives at more frequent intervals. The 1975 venture, the largest ever to be undertaken by the Bureau in a non-"0" year, will cost $45,000,000 and cover 1 million households.

Revenue-sharing, moreover, flushed out several small communities of whose existence the Bureau hadn't even been aware. A couple of years before each decennial enumeration gets under way, the Bureau writes to every known municipality inquiring about the changes, if any, in its legal boundaries; and it also beseeches from the administrators of every county a list of every incorporated place within *its* boundaries. Counties, however, not unlike people, do not always answer their mail; and besides, in the 1960s or earlier, some geographical entities that were technically incorporated had more or less just closed up shop and ceased to function.

With revenue-sharing available, though, long-dormant municipalities suddenly shook themselves into wakefulness and emerged into the light with hands outstretched. Concurrently, the mayors and selectmen of well-defined and well-recognized communities from coast to coast decided that their constituencies had been lamentably undercounted, and they descended on Suitland in force, occasionally flanked by Senators or Representatives or both. (There is no record of any local government's maintaining it was credited with an excess of population.) As a result of such petitions, and at the expense of the petitioners, between April 1, 1970, and December 31, 1972, the

Bureau took 141 special censuses of aggrieved communities. (The Bureau charges $20 for a 100-person count; between $1,000 and $1,020 for 1,000 people; $7,165 to $7,795 for 20,000; $12,840 to $14,200 for 40,000; and so on. Recounts do not come cheap.) Bull Schoals, Arkansas, provided the most spectacular outcome: Its official population went up by 129.1 percent—from 392 to 898. North Riverside, Illinois, shrank from 8,097 to 7,849. These recounts didn't do most of the places that asked for them much financial good, because it was the policy of the United States Treasury, and of a good many states, not to amend their lower-level fund-sharing distributions unless all the political units in the same county were recounted at the same time.

As an example of a spot that felt it might have been short-counted and consequently short-changed, let us have a look at Provincetown, Massachusetts, a small, ocean-girded township on the tip of Cape Cod. We can learn a good deal about a place like Provincetown from 1970 Census tables—just about the same as what we can learn about every place with a population of between 2,500 and 10,000. (There are 4,134 such places in the United States.) We learn that all but seventy-five of Provincetown's 2,911 credited residents lived in the center of town. Their median age was high. The median for the state of Massachusetts was twenty-nine; for Provincetown, 39.3—36.2 for men and 41.9 for women. Females outnumbered males, 1,514 to 1,397, and there were more than twice as many females sixty-five years or older as there were males—262 to 121. There were 716 individuals under eighteen, rather a scarcity of young people; thus, the average number of persons per household was a low 2.41, in contrast to the 3.44 figure for Barnstable County, which includes the whole of Cape Cod. And on Census Day there were only thirty-six non-whites in Provincetown.

In a settlement that goes back to 1620, when the Pilgrims made Provincetown their first landing-place, it is no surprise that there are old buildings; it was not in conformity with the national pattern, however, that, of Provincetown's 1,430 year-round housing units (the place also has many summer homes), 1,266 were built in 1939 or earlier, and only fifteen after 1969. For only 402 of the 1,190 occupied housing units was access to an automobile reported, but this radical departure from the American norm was understandable when we further perceived that Provincetown Center covers only 1.6 square miles.

And so the statistics marched along: 2,704 native Americans on hand (1,765 of them born in Massachusetts); 197 persons born abroad (here the Census left us in the dark, but we know that the bulk of them are likely to be from Portugal, whence most of Provincetown's fishermen have perennially emigrated); 222 persons twenty-five and over who had had four or more years of college; median school years completed for everybody: exactly twelve; 949 males over sixteen who worked in the year before the Census, but only 414 who worked full-time; 652 such females, but nearly two thirds of them (many, no doubt, employees of seasonal tourist restaurants) with less than a half year's employment; median income—very low—$7,177 per family; 92 families— 13.4 percent of all Provincetown's families—with incomes below the poverty level.

So much for the basic facts. But the most puzzling statistic, to many people who cared about that particular community, was the crucial one—that total population figure of 2,911. By the Census Bureau's measurements, the population had been 3,389 in 1960, and while the place was undeniably in the economic doldrums—the fishing business was bad, and that had long been the principal source of livelihood for the year-rounders—it seemed hard to believe that the population had decreased.

The editors of the weekly Provincetown *Advocate*, indeed, thought that the population had gone *up*, perhaps as far as 5,000; and what concerned them was that if it had, or if it had even stayed constant, Provincetown was receiving far less than its due share under the federal revenue-sharing program. How could there be only 2,911 people around in 1970, they wondered, including those 716 then under voting age, when in 1972 there were 3,416 registered *voters* in town? Could there be that many summer people who ignored Provincetown in April but returned in November to cast their votes? Wasn't it more likely that the census-takers on the scene, its circumscribed area notwithstanding, had overlooked a lot of people living at the end of the narrow, twisting alleys for which, among other things, the spot is celebrated? When the matter was brought to the attention of one high-ranking Census Bureau official, he replied, *inter alia,* in the course of a private letter:

On the uncertain assumption that the population of Provincetown had changed very little between 1970 and 1972, [the *Advocate*] argues that the 60 per cent increase in registration [between 1970 and 1972] represents a large upswing in voter participation of persons who lived there in 1970 and, therefore, the 1970 population must have been larger than that counted in the Census. An equally plausible (but possibly naive) explanation of the registration figures would be that the population of Provincetown increased by approximately 60 per cent between April, 1970, and the summer of 1972. Provincetown, as a resort area, has a large transient population, and it is possible that recent court decisions modifying attitudes toward eligibility for voter registration resulted in a large number of the transient "concerned" youth registering prior to the 1972 election. However, reasonable doubt exists as to whether they lived there in April, 1970, or for that matter could be found there in April, 1973.

In short, our experience with voter registration figures leads us to believe that they are not good indicators of the size of the total population of an area. The hypotheses presented above are sheer speculation and it would require intensive study to establish a valid interpretation of the registration figures. It would be interesting, for example, to determine how many of the persons added to the voter lists between 1970 and 1972 could be located in Provincetown in April, 1973.

The Census enumeration began with a carefully checked list of all the addresses of residential quarters in the town. Census questionnaires were mailed to those addresses. As the questionnaires were mailed they were checked off the list. After a suitable period of time, follow-up enumerators were assigned to make personal visits to the addresses from which no questionnaires had been mailed back and the information was collected by telephone calls, additional visits, and, as a last resort, interviews with neighbors to obtain as much information as possible. In short, the procedure insured complete coverage of the area.

Finally, as a general rule, we find that reports from respondents that they never received schedules are not reliable. Although a decennial census is a memorable event for a member of the Census staff, it is clearly not such an event for the respondents, particularly when asked to recall their participation more than two years after the event. Information may be obtained from one member of the household who may or may not have reported the visit to the other members, or it may have been obtained from neighbors. Our investigations of numerous complaints of this type indicate that, for the most part, persons who report they have not been enumerated actually have been.

Provincetown did not commission the Bureau to make a special re-enumeration. For one thing, it is one of merely sixteen townships in Barnstable County, and unless all the others had taken similar action a federal recount would have resulted in no further federal funds. For another, a *state* census-taken in 1971 had credited Provincetown with only 2,732 year-round residents, considerably fewer than the Bureau's 1970 figure of 2,911. But the Massachusetts tabulation had been conducted, in between other chores, by local policemen, and Provincetown was not satisfied that they had poked into every cranny where someone might be living.

In the spring of 1973, accordingly, Provincetown conducted its own Census, designed to cover only individuals seventeen years or older. The total of *them* came to 3,123. When the town officials added to that number the 850 residents under seventeen it was convinced were on the scene (the 1970 Census had put the number under eighteen at 716), it ended up with a grand total of 3,973—1,241 more than the state had granted it in 1971, and 1,062 more than the official federal figure of 1970. There was little likelihood that, by births or net in-migrations, the town had acquired that many newcomers in three years.

The Bureau knows that certain slipups are inevitable and unavoidable, and it tries to minimize them as much as possible. So concerned, indeed, has it been over the years to catch up with its theoretically most qualified informants—the people it sees in person—that it has even conducted surveys to determine when it is most likely to find them at home. The results would not appear to bode well for future enumerators; fewer and fewer Americans can be classified as homebodies. In 1960, for instance, the Bureau determined that between 8 A.M. and 3 P.M. it was possible to find someone over fourteen (presumably the cutoff point for a provider of reliable data) in from 67 to 71 percent of all our residences; and between 4 P.M. and 9 P.M. (presumably the latest hour at which an investigative call is tolerable) in from 72 to 80 percent of them. But, when a similar survey was made late in 1971, during the earlier hours only 56 to 59 percent of the residences had a responsible spokesman available; and during the later hours only 70 to 78 percent had one.

With nearly 200,000 fallible human beings involved in its preparation, there were bound to be plain errors in the 1970 Census. These, by Bureau speculation, probably produced erroneous data for 4,900,000 individuals, or 2.4 percent of the total accepted population. (The figure given to President Nixon on December 1, 1970, was later found to be too small itself, not even counting the subsequent revelation of an undercount, but by so trifling a sum—23,372 individuals—that it didn't make any appreciable difference from a national point of view, and a margin of error indeed that the Bureau would gladly settle for in all its compilations.) Some of the mistakes resulted from the laziness, carelessness, or even stupidity of enumerators who, sent out to scour a certain territory, prove more disposed to gab with people than to tab them. With part-time help, misreporting is in any event perhaps unavoidable.

Whatever the case, census-takers do not ask to see birth certificates, so there was almost certainly an undercount of illegitimate children and of women over fifty. And, because of the way the 1970 Census forms were devised, there was no handy means of indicating any birth date before 1860. Thus, one of the murkiest areas of knowledge involves those exceptionally senior senior citizens who are over one hundred and ten. Moreover, with the forms designed so that the information inscribed on them could, via the FOSDIC device, be electronically scanned and processed, if somewhere along the line a human hand happened to spill coffee on a form, the poor scanner could get hopelessly addled and transform the most venerable of centenarians into an infant with a bar sinister.

When it came to the matter of undercounts, some blacks have maintained that there was a deliberate plan to omit large numbers of them from the national tabulation in 1970. The Bureau contends, contrarily, that most blacks weren't even aware of the existence of undercoverage, let alone the extent of it, until Census officials publicly called attention to it themselves. In any event, a disproportionate number of the people who did get missed were black. They constituted only 11 percent of the population, but the Bureau's guess is that of the 5,300,000 individuals it very likely ignored 1,880,000, or 35 percent, were black. There were far more whites—3,450,000 of them—who were also missed, but they represented a mere 1.9 percent of the total white population, whereas the missing blacks amounted to 7.7 percent of the black total.

In the hearts of black ghettos, which even black census-takers were sometimes reluctant to explore with perseverance, the undercount may have run as high as 10 or 15 percent. It could occasionally seem more prudent to assume that there was nobody living inside a run-down building than to enter it to make sure.

A supervisor who set forth to check on his employees' performance in an urban ghetto in 1960 had reported, *inter alia,*

One of the addresses to which I obtained access had been marked in the listing book as follows: "Will not return—something thrown at me." The occupants of the house with the "vacant" apartments were a sullen group. The bleary-eyed household head of the first floor apartment had a bottle on the table and glared silently at me while his wife answered the questions. . . . My experiences apparently were prosaic compared to some I learned about from discussions with crew leaders and enumerators, e.g. the lady who blundered into the house full of dope addicts; another lady who had been chased out of a house by a threatening occupant ... Although this sort of experience is not a regular occurrence by any means, it need happen to an enumerator only once to be unnerving. Situations in which an enumerator is in real danger probably are rare—but cases of suspicion, sullenness, and vituperative hostility in this area are far above our expected norm. It makes the recruitment and retention of good enumerators exceedingly difficult—and those we do retain are necessarily those with strong backs and strong stomachs— their intellectual ability being an incidental or accidental asset. . . . The inevitable concomitant of these conditions is under-enumeration—of both persons and housing units. No enumerator in her right mind, even if she is being paid at an hourly rate, will go through some of the traumatic experiences necessary to do a good job of coverage.*

Another ghetto enumerator felt constrained to report, without counting them individually, the presence of "an abundant roach population which interfered with the interview by crawling all over the interviewer and her forms." †

If people refuse to welcome, or even tolerate, the

---

* Pritzker and Rothwell, p. 14.
† Pritzker and Rothwell, p. 15.

presence of an enumerator, there is not much he or
she can do about it. "We don't carry search warrants,
after all," Conrad Taeuber, the chief demographer of
the 1970 Census, said in conversation, "but we like to
think we got to all the people that we could. We went
to every place where people might normally live, but
we didn't inspect every automobile or hallway or
all-night movie. Fortunately, it's cold enough in
April, as a rule, so that there are few people sleeping
in the streets." Then, too, there are a lot of people in
April or any other time of year who are illegal aliens
or other fugitives from the law, and it is difficult to
get them to sit still for a chat about vital statistics.
Census Bureau employees sometimes jokingly say
that what they need is a special corps of undercover
operatives to handle undercoverage.

Most of the blacks omitted from the 1970 Census
were thought to be males between twenty and fifty
years old, a group of comparatively high mobility.
Some of these who were never officially tabulated
were visibly extant. An enumerator might go into a
home, for instance, and find a woman, some children,
and an adult man in his undershirt. The woman
would identify herself as the head of the household
and the children as her offspring. And who was the
gentleman on the couch drinking the beer and
watching the television? Oh, he was just a friend who
happened to be passing by. Or a cousin from out of
town. Or a shrug.

Because so many black males (who by statistical
evidence had to exist and in physical terms plainly

did exist) were never counted, all the Census's statistics on male–female ratios were unhappily skewed. When the 1970 Census reported that in Alaska there were 119 men for every hundred women, the ratio was probably quite accurate, for in that state, Eskimos and Aleuts aside, there were comparatively few non-whites. But the published ratio for New York—only 91.5 males for every 100 females—was implausibly low; and similar male undercounts in other big cities made the official countrywide ratio—ninety-five males per 100 females—open to question.

In 1940, incidentally, the final tabulation had put males ahead—101 to 100. Even if all the uncounted males of 1970 had been fed into the computers, women would still have outnumbered them. For, whereas in 1920 women outlived men, on the average, by only one year, they now outlive them by seven. Presumably the stresses to which males are or believe themselves to be exposed account for their earlier demise; it will be interesting to see whether, as women demand and receive more responsibilities, their relative durability will be affected.

One well-known adult black male, the comedian Dick Gregory, asserted in *Ebony* in 1971 that he and his wife and their children—eight of these at 1970 census-taking time—had *never* been counted in *any* census. The Census Bureau declined to reply to his charge; to have done so, it argued, would have constituted a violation of its rules about confidentiality. It was possible that some neighbor of the

Gregorys told an enumerator about their ménage; indeed, in 1970, the net estimated undercount had to be reduced by an *over*count of 400,000 or so people who had both been enumerated in person and identified by others. The omission of the Gregorys, if it actually occurred, took place in spite of a concentrated effort by the Bureau to persuade blacks that it was very much to their advantage to be included in the official version of the population. Even before municipal revenue-sharing, there were certain tax moneys allocated to states according to the number of people who lived in them; and then there was also, of course, the matter of added representation in the Congress; conceivably, if every missing person in a state were counted, it could move from the four hundred thirty-sixth place on the seat-apportionment roster to the four hundred thirty-fifth.

So the Bureau, taking note of the increasing tendency throughout the country for minority groups to assert their differences rather than be melted in a pot, began long before enumeration time in 1970 to urge everyone to stand up and be counted. In the case of blacks, it asked disk jockeys on soul stations to spread the word, and it invited all sorts of organizations—the Urban League, the N.A.A.C.P., the Muslims, the Panthers, anyone it could get hold of—to distribute special hortatory literature it worked up for the occasion, brimming with supposedly slangy appeals like "Do your thing!," "Let's get it together," and "On Census Day, Say it Loud and Clear—I'm Black, I'm Proud—and I AM HERE!"

There was no way of telling how directly effective such appeals were, but it heartened the Census people who distributed them that, whereas in the 1960 count some 15 percent of all black males between fifteen and twenty-four had been over-looked, the missing-person proportion of that particular category was down in 1970 to 8 percent.

Imprecise as the Census figures may be, they are probably the best we have. "Whatever our limitations," one Bureau official remarked in conversation,

at least they're uniform for the country. We play a kind of game of history here, with a snapshot taken once every ten years—a rather blurred snapshot at that, inasmuch as our data are imperfect and statistics won't answer everything. And when you think you've learned something unique it may on re-examination turn out to be just dirt on the electronic scanner. Furthermore, the census is like a live television show and unlike a taped one: it's a one-shot thing—a very massive and infinitely refined one-shot, to be sure—and if you make a fluff you can't shoot it over. We have to set up an operation on the scale of General Motors every ten years, and then we produce one car and quit.

Some of the minor mishaps one hears of in connection with the Census are ludicrous: the case of the wealthy, cultured, patrician lady, for instance, who was recorded as an illiterate because she said, quite truthfully, that she had never attended any school; she had been privately tutored at home. But when more than 200 million people are involved in a massive statistical study, it is not unreasonable to suppose that in the end there are many such minor mistakes in all directions and that when they are averaged up most of them cancel each other out. And these averages—for population trends, birth and death rates, income levels, school enrollments, and so on—are not to be taken lightly. For they are the yardsticks by which we can most readily perceive some of the strengths and weaknesses of our nation. So the Census, its deficiencies notwithstanding, remains, at every ten-year pause in our history, our best means for ascertaining, at least quantitatively, who and what and where we really are.

IV

☆ ☆ ☆ ☆ ☆ ☆

America in Drift

W<small>HEN THE FIRST</small> C<small>ENSUS WAS TAKEN IN</small> 1790, 95 percent of the population of the United States was rural. A half century later, the country was still 90 percent rural and, a whole century later, two thirds. By the start of the twentieth century, the gap between rural and urban residents was beginning to narrow. The country mice still outnumbered the city mice, 45,835,000 to 30,160,000, but the great national drift from the sticks to the sidewalks was inexorably under way. The native-born whites of America, traditional tillers (not to mention owners) of the soil, were the most reluctant, or at any rate the slowest, to embrace urban life; whereas by 1960 87.5 percent of all foreign-born whites on hand were urban, and 73.2 percent of all blacks, only 68 percent of the native whites were in that category.

Nowadays we hear much of megalopolises—all but continuous urban belts of the country extending from, say, Portland, Maine, to Richmond, Virginia. It is true enough that in 1970 almost 150 million urban folk were jammed together on merely 54,103 of our 3,536,855 square miles of land. (This was about 1.5 percent of all our land and, if it were all lumped together, would have constituted an area roughly the size of Florida.) It was true, too, that, like lemmings, we had been flocking increasingly from our plains and mountains to our shores. More than half the population of the United States resided within fifty miles of an ocean, a gulf, or a Great Lake, which meant, for most people, an easy one-hour drive. One did not have to consult the Census to be aware that there were some 30 million people within striking distance of the Atlantic Coast alone; one needed only to inspect the Cape Cod National Seashore on an August weekend. In 1950, incidentally, when the population of the United States was 150,697,361, there were 33,253,000 visits to all our national parks together. Twenty years later, there was just about one such visit annually for every living American. Perhaps it was indicative of an upgrading of American life—or perhaps merely of better roads—that we had in a generation, person by person, multiplied our use of our parks fivefold. Of course, this was tough on the parks.

Yet one needed only to fly from Boston to New York, or from New York to Washington, to observe (on a clear day, from a window seat) how surprisingly much of this heavily populated megapolitan space looked uninhabited. In fact, owing to abandoned farms, there was probably more unused acreage along these routes than there had been fifty years before. Of this littoral stretch and its immediate inland environs, not more than 9 percent of the earth had yet been urbanized, and only about the same amount again would be required if, by the year 2000, the population were to increase by half again its present size.

Barring some upheaval in our national predilections, further such consolidation will almost surely occur, because in recent years there has been no random ebb and flow of population—rather, a steady, almost gravitational pull toward the big cities, most of which touch water. The lure of the metropolis is, of course, worldwide, and it can be stemmed only in countries like China or Tanzania, where the governments can tell their citizens where to live. The proponents of resettlement schemes in America know better than to hope that any meaningful number of our citizenry, for all that they are a people on wheels in a land of highways, will ever be content to return to self-contained small-town life. In 1960, 47 million Americans lived in metropolitan areas each of which had at least 2 million inhabitants; now, 52 million do. In 1970, the state of Texas, for all its vaunted spaciousness, contained twenty-four of the country's 243 metropolitan areas that had a population of 50,000 or more; in the 1960s, 98 percent of Texas's population growth occurred in those two dozen communities.

How drastic the shift has been in this century can be spelled out in many ways: for instance, the urban areas that in 1970 harbored 73.5 percent of the entire population had in 1900 just 40 percent of it. And, if one examines the comparable figures for the black segment of the population, the change since 1900 seems even more striking. At the start of this century, there were 6,482,000 blacks *outside* urban areas, and in 1970, 5,809,679 of them; in seventy years, the black rural population had had consistently high birth rates and increasingly low death rates, but nonetheless its numbers had actually diminished.

To take pressure off our existing cities in the years ahead will require some national planning, and prodding, on quite a scale. By the end of the twentieth century, there may be another 75 million or so Americans, and unless they are spectacularly different from their parents and grandparents, 55 million of them will choose to enjoy the delights, and ignore the deterrents, of metropolitan life. To build new cities for them is easy enough, in theory. We already have the roads to connect these settlements, as a result of the vast interstate highway program that the Congress initiated in 1956. Some of these roads, to be sure, seem to have had little effect so far on peoples' residential choices—U.S. 80, for example, a fine, relatively little-used thoroughfare that traverses a wilderness of northern Pennsylvania. Up to now, its main discernible *raison d'être* (aside from giving Pennsylvania a fat slice of the highway-funds pie) seems to have been to expedite motor travel between New Jersey and California, which is not an over-whelming justification, inasmuch as the average automobile trip in the United States is less than ten miles.

But elsewhere the highway system has had an impact on the flow of people as well as of cars. The *non*metropolitan portions of the country are growing more slowly than the national average. But those that were crossed by an expressway and that also contained at least one urban center of 25,000 people grew, between 1960 and 1970, at the same rate as the whole nation. This state of affairs is encouraging to planners pondering methods of accommodating 60 million extra bodies in places other than our present-day cities. But there are also discouraging aspects. To house all 55 million would entail the construction of two new 95,000-person cities every month until the turn of the century.

There were twice as many Americans alive in 1970 as in 1920. More than 90 percent of the surplus settled in metropolitan areas. Four fifths of the permanent shift of our population between 1960 and 1970 has been from rural to urban settings, and four fifths of *that* to the suburbs, now unchallengeably the spot where more of America sleeps than in either the central cities or the rural areas. Nobody has ever been able to agree on a national flower or tree representative of the country as a whole; a claim might now logically be put in for crabgrass.

There is nothing very dashing or daring any more about moving to the suburbs, but Americans apparently no longer want to be trail-blazers. They want to be where everybody else is; to live in a suburb and for a change to visit Disneyland or Disneyworld. Most important, they want to be where the jobs are.

Our metropolitan areas may be crowded, dirty, polluted, unsafe, traffic-snarled, and hard on the nerves; but, if what people do is a fair reflection of how they feel, then that is clearly where they wish to live. The only significant change in their preferences would seem to be that instead of moving into the middle of an established community they would rather park at its edge.

Half of the people of the United States live in just eight of the fifty states—California, Illinois, Massachusetts, Michigan, New Jersey, New York, Ohio, and Pennsylvania. Most of them, furthermore, live in or just outside the big cities of these states. Sixteen million of them alone live in what is sometimes called the commutershed of New York City. In 1970, New Jersey, a considerable part of which lies within that commutershed, for the first time displaced Rhode Island as the state with the highest density of population. New Jersey had nearly a thousand people per square mile. Alaska had fewer than one. (The density for the Upper Yukon Division of Alaska, an 84,142-square-mile expanse that is larger than forty of the states but that in 1970 could muster only 1,666 inhabitants, was .02.) The density for the entire United States was fifty-eight per square mile; by way of comparison, the figure for Japan was 720, and for Belgium 822. Yet within the metropolitan areas themselves, one effect of the huge suburban sprawl had been to *reduce* the density of population—from 6,580 people per square mile in 1920, when the suburbs were inconsequential, to 3,376 a half century afterward. The density per square mile for Manhattan Island, the acme of urbanism, shrank from 103,822 to 67,808.

Nearly 51 million people—26 percent of the native population—lived in a state other than the one they were born in. This was par for the American course; the United States had long been a realm of rovers. Even in 1850, one in every four Americans was living outside the state of his birth. In 1950, more than half the residents of Arizona, California, Nevada, Oregon, and Washington were migrants. Some of them, to be sure, had merely moved from one Western state to another.

For all that there has been a massive westward drift, though, by 1970 the East Coast had hardly capitulated: About 25 percent of all Americans lived along the Altantic seaboard 100 years earlier, and about 25 percent still did. Median population centers may crawl toward the Pacific, but psychologically the Atlantic remains the American hearth. California may have more people now, more cars, more oranges, more sunshine, and more smog than New York, but prime television time is still determined by the eating and sleeping habits of the East.

An overhasty perusal of Census figures could lead to the conclusion that Americans skip around even more than they actually do. While about 20 percent of them have changed homes every year since 1948, of the 36 million Americans who now move annually, only one fifth switch states, and nearly two thirds don't even cross a county line. It is still possible to read in a Cape Cod weekly of a seventy-five-year-old man born in Plymouth who has never wandered farther afield than Eastham, an hour's drive away.

He is by no means unique. There were over 12 million Americans in 1970—6.1 percent of everybody—who for more than twenty years had always lived in the same house. Among those folk whose residential roots were firmly fixed, New Mexico—with a heavy and stable quotient of Indians—had the highest proportion: 9.3 percent. Nevada, Oregon, and California ranked low, each with 3.3 percent. Not counting the West Coast, more than 8 percent of all Americans hadn't changed homes between 1949 and 1970. And 53 percent of the population five years old or older was occupying the same residence in 1970 as in 1965. For New England, it was 60 percent, for the north central states 54.8 percent, for the South, 50.8 percent, and for the West 44.1 percent.

Even 51.3 percent of the urban population, which is more likely to pack up and move than its rural counterpart, hadn't switched residences in five years. Pennsylvania, with a 64 percent rating, led all the states in this respect, and led them, paradoxically, even though between 1960 and 1970 it was the state that had the highest numerical net loss of population —400,000—of any state in the Union.

Nevertheless, 83 percent of all living Americans born in Pennsylvania still called that state home. Whereas for the entire nation 8.6 percent of the people moved out of the state of their birth between 1965 and 1970, for Pennsylvania it was only 4.7

percent. And whereas 17.1 percent of all Americans moved *somewhere*, if only around the corner, for Pennsylvania the figure was only 10.4 percent. The comparative stability, or stolidity, of Pennsylvanians can be indicated by still another measurement: More than half the 1970 housing units in Nevada, for instance, had been built since 1960; only 15.4 percent of those in Pennsylvania were as new as that.

Notwithstanding, there has been a considerable amount of changing residences, and it still goes on. Between March 1970 and March 1971, 36,161,000 people moved—17.9 percent of the population. But the majority of these migrants—23 million of them— merely moved to another place within the same county. Much of the American migration, thus, is very narrow in scope. In 1900, the percentage of the native population born in a state other than its state of current residence was 20.6; the proportion rose to 26.4 by 1960; but in the decade that followed it dwindled, if by only a tiny fraction, to 26.3.

Ever since 1880, more than 20 percent of the population has ended up living in a non-native state. In 1900, there were twenty states more than 80 percent of whose inhabitants had been born within their borders. In 1930, there were eleven; in 1960, only four (California, Michigan, New York, and Ohio). But there have been changes in the nature of migration. People used to move—in the main, westward—until they found a place where they settled down more or less permanently. Now they tend to move in every which direction and less frequently to stay put, even when they retire. And they move more than Census figures disclose, for if an individual makes half a dozen moves within any period of investigation he is still counted as merely one mover.

How the pattern of westward movement and fixed settlement has lately been altered can be readily shown: In 1890, only one in every thirty people who had been born west of the Mississippi had bucked the national tide and was living east of the river. By 1960, 7 percent of those born beyond its western banks had elected to live east of it. So within the major East-to-West flow there developed a marked counter-current of West-to-East migration.

The reason was probably obvious: Once we had pushed out and reached the Pacific Coast, there was nowhere left for us to go except Alaska and Hawaii, and they were awfully far away—far enough, at least, so that between 1965 and 1970 Alaska welcomed a net in-migration of only 21,427 people over five years of age, and Hawaii of only 13,289. California, of course, had perennially been the mecca of migrant Americans, but the pace of pilgrimage to it had markedly abated. In 1970, 9.2 percent of the population of California consisted of new arrivals since 1965, but this was not much above the national average for all states of 8.6 percent. California actually attracted no greater a proportion of new-comers than Connecticut, over this stretch, and it lagged in percentage figures behind thirty-two other states—behind Nevada, for one, with 24.7 percent of *its* population having arrived in that five-year period, and behind Florida, with 18.5 percent.

Perhaps the Western coastal states were approaching the saturation point. In any event, there was between 1965 and 1970 a higher proportion of newcomers flocking to Arizona, Colorado, Idaho, and Wyoming, along with Nevada, than to either Oregon or Washington. We are dealing here, it should be quickly added, in percentages; in actual numbers of migrants, California continued to lead the nation, with 318,214 arrivals from other states in the five years; its closest competitors were Florida, Texas, and Virginia, and the Virginia figures were in large part the result of whites leaving Washington, D.C., for the nearby suburbs, as blacks replaced them within the capital city.

One reason why cities like Washington are getting constantly blacker is that it costs money to move, and blacks as a group simply don't have enough means to emulate white Americans in mobility. There is an important exception—the blacks who have practically no means at all. Whatever any American's color, the likelihood of his pulling up stakes also relates closely to the extent of his education. Eight percent of all men who have had four years of college now annually migrate across a county line, whereas only 3 percent of those who haven't finished high school do. It is the comparatively better-educated whites and the comparatively less-well-educated blacks who move the most—the first group principally because they have better job offers, the second because they have none. Our national mobility is all at once a combination of the migration of those who, aspiring to an even higher standard of living than they enjoy, can afford to pull up stakes; and of those who, realizing that they could not be much worse off than they are, cannot afford not to.

Our most vigorous migrants have been those not encumbered by domestic responsibilities, who can move in a Volkswagen instead of a van. The peak of mobility is reached by the twenty-two to twenty-four-year-old age group. Nearly half of them move every year—males a trifle more intensively than females. When the sexes get together, they *really* move. Eighty-four percent of Americans on first getting married change their residence. But hold! The surprising thing about this statistic is that when 16 percent first get married, they don't change. Mothers-in-law are still a formidable factor of the American way of life.

Throughout the nation, blacks have tended to change residences slightly more frequently than do whites (being on the whole less agreeably housed, they have less reason to cherish their former surroundings), but they do not move quite so far. The big northward drift of blacks that has sharply altered the nature of most large American cities was only in part the result of dissatisfaction with Southern segregation. It is not so much social stress as economic stress that makes most people migrate—the Second World War Jews of Europe being, of course, somewhat of an exception—and the move to the North really began during the First World War, when immigration to this country from Europe was severely curtailed and many industrial jobs opened up to blacks north of the Mason-Dixon Line.

They crossed it at such a clip that after the results of the 1920 Census were in, Congress, under pressure from the Southern members of the House, refused to exercise its historical obligation to reapportion. Too many rural Congressmen from below the Line would have lost their seats as the result of the defection of black constituents who, though for the most part they could not vote, had always been included in the regional head count. One Mississippi Representative argued then that the out-migration was only temporary; the blacks would all soon come back to their birthplaces; until they did, wherever they happened to be living, they should be credited to Mississippi.

Of course, they never came back. Instead, they were emulated on a large scale. Between 1940 and 1960, the rural South lost 3 million blacks to the urban North. By now, indeed, there is no more statistical reason for associating a huge number of black Americans with the South than for inseparably linking any assimilated immigrants with the land of their ancestors. For in 1970 less than half of the black population of the United States living outside the South was born in the South. And, for the entire black population, in just the ten years between 1960 and 1970, the percentage that was Southern-born dropped from 79 to 70. The northward trek is slowing down. Between 1960 and 1970, the net out-migration of rural Southern blacks was only 1,400,000. Over the decade, the annual rate of exodus of black males between fifteen and twenty-four from Mississippi dropped from 70,000 to 30,000. Naturally, there were fewer of them by then to leave, and there were fewer jobs to seek up North. Also, although Southern wage-earners now average about $2,000 a year less than their Northern counterparts, their living costs are generally lower.

More and more, blacks are moving not to the North but staying in the South and moving within its confines from rural to urban settings. In 1900, of the 8,834,000 blacks then in the country, 7,923,000 were Southern, and of them only 17.2 percent urban. Seventy years later, of the 11,970,000 blacks in the South, nearly three quarters were urban. (Of those up North, 95 percent were urban.) The South, like every section of the country, increased its population in the 1960s, but the nonmetropolitan South—the historic home of most Southern blacks—had a natural increase (births minus deaths) of 1,071,000, and yet despite that ended up, so heavy was the out-migration of older blacks, with a net population *decrease* of 269,000.

There has been a change, too, in the pattern of employment in the Northern cities. Where once they offered plenty of jobs to unskilled workers, now these jobs are diminishing, and the demand is for skills that the rural Southerners, whatever their color, do not often possess. Whereas in the 1940s and 1950s the big metropolitan areas of the north central states—principally, Detroit and Chicago—experienced a net gain in population, from migration, of 1 million people each decade, between 1960 and 1970 their black influx just about balanced their white outflux. The fact that the Northern centers appeared to have very little in the way of amenities—at any rate, by white criteria—to offer arriving blacks was probably of no account. Harlem at its dingiest might look pretty good to an Alabama farmhand. Human beings like company, and miserable ones perhaps even more. The black ghettos may be thronged with pushers and pimps, but at least these are *people.* One can live on an Alabama farm and not see a dozen other persons in a month.

There is still a very definable Black Belt in the United States. It begins in eastern Texas and sweeps along the Gulf and Atlantic coasts, curving northward and finally, after cutting across eighteen states in all, terminating in Massachusetts. Yet there are heavy concentrations of blacks well outside the basic belt. In 1940, blacks accounted for just 1 percent of the population of the West. In 1970, 8 percent of that region was black. Between 1960 and 1970, the black population of Compton, California, increased by 100 percent; Compton, with a total population of 78,611, ended up 71 percent black. Willowbrook, California, with 28,705 people, was 83 percent black. Across the country, within the fifty-seven metropolises that had 500,000 or more inhabitants, the black proportion rose in the decade from 18 to 23 percent. In

THE AMERICAN PEOPLE

metropolitan areas with more than 2 million people, blacks represented 28 percent of the total. By contrast, in the *non*metropolitan areas of the northeastern, the north central, and the Western states, they represented less than 1 percent.

Between 1920 and 1960, as blacks streamed out of the South, the total population growth of that region was markedly arrested—its headway consisting merely of the extent to which its excess of births over deaths could offset its migration losses. But after 1960, a new national migratory trend developed—a North–South pendulum swinging in counterpoint to the East–West momentum. Specifically, in exchange for the 1,400,000 blacks the South lost to the North in that decade, the South gained 1,800,000 whites. It was the first time in sixty years that the South could boast a net migratory plus. Florida led the way, with 1,340,000 whites, many of them elderly, pouring in. But the trend was widespread. In the 1940s, and again in the 1950s, eight Southern states—Alabama, Arkansas, Georgia, Louisiana, Mississippi, North Carolina, South Carolina, and Tennessee—had among them each time lost 800,000 blacks. In the next decade, they gained *in toto* 400,000 whites.

Where did they all come from? For the first time in the history of the state of New York, for one thing, there was a net migratory loss. While a net of 400,000 blacks moved in, a net of 600,000 whites moved out. New York City was chiefly responsible. Over that ten-year stretch, it lost nearly 1 million white migrants (not all of them to the South), and it gained

nearly 500,000 blacks (few of them from anywhere
except the South). There was also a substantial gain
from the excess, among already resident blacks, of
births over deaths. The situation in other states with
large municipalities was similar. Illinois gained
125,000 blacks but lost 200,000 whites; Ohio took in
45,000 extra blacks and gave up 190,000 whites.

Where did they go? Well, in an 11-million-person
area of New York state that included New York City
and four outlying counties, of the 888,316 individuals
who emigrated between 1965 and 1970 (at the same
time that 302,856 migrants moved in), only 126,978
followed the usual pattern of moving to another place
within the state itself; almost as many—124,020 of
them—went to Florida, whence a mere relative
trickle of people—17,069 of *them*—betook themselves
to New York.

The only Census category in which the New York
urban area gained in the five years was among black
females between fifteen and twenty-four. The only
states that sent more people to this New York area
than they received from it were Alabama and Mississippi; California, by contrast, got 81,654 of these
New Yorkers in exchange for 25,522 of its own
people; Arizona got 7,831 of them and yielded up
only 1,698. More than 60,000 of the New York
defectors went to the west coast of Florida, which in
turn lost 8,311 people to the New York area. That
part of Florida sent 372 to North Dakota and
received 377—practically a standoff. Between all of
Florida and all of California there was another nearly

even swap—54,986 Floridians becoming Californians and 50,744 Californians taking their places.

Between Greater Los Angeles and Greater New York City there was a marked disparity—the former gaining 44,862 migrants from the latter and ceding to it only 12,838. But otherwise, in a purely statistical sense, a case could be made that the two rival ports were peas in the same pod. New York enjoyed a commanding lead in retail sales—$12 billion to $5 billion—but if one compared the two places according to a half dozen arbitrarily selected statistics—say, stability of population, level of education, crowdedness of homes, availability of dentists, extent of burglaries, and cumulative fertility rates—they came out virtually identical. And even the crucial yardstick, median family income, gave the seemingly more popular Los Angeles only a trifling edge as of 1970—$10,972 to the $10,870 of New York. That difference would hardly seem to have justified the cost of moving.

Much of the outflux from the New York City area between 1965 and 1970 consisted of elderly people; 88,643 of them left, and only 14,329 of their age-group cohorts arrived. (While 47,149 of these New Yorkers over sixty-five descended on Miami, a mere 7,121 Miamians of *all* ages made the move to New York.) Examining Census data for the west coast of Florida, one found a net in-migration, between 1965 and 1970, of 35,650 males over sixty-five and 27,688 females over sixty-five.

"Ahah!" one surmised at first glance, "an ideal

spot for widows seeking new husbands!" But at a
second glance one perceived that during the same
years there was a net influx to that Gulf coast of
33,080 females between forty-five and sixty-four, and
only 27,320 males in that relatively younger group.
Was one then to infer, perhaps uncharitably, that a
good many of the older men brought along substantially younger wives or female companions, and that
the older widows were out of luck? Virtually all these
new Floridians were white. For the Gulf coast
regions, there was a net influx in the second half of
the 1960s of a mere twelve black males over sixty-five
and 192 females in the same age group—some of
these latter, one suspected, being elderly white northern widows' faithful family retainers.

V

☆　☆　☆　☆　☆　☆

The Not-So-Sunny South

FOR THE COUNTRY AS A WHOLE, THE ANNUAL NET out-migration from rural to urban areas came to about 11 million people between 1940 and 1960. Between 1960 and 1970, the urban gains from migration were pared to 2,500,000. Among Standard Metropolitan Statistical Areas containing more than 200,000 residents, the biggest advance was scored by the Anaheim–Santa Ana Grove area in California, which includes Disneyland (up 551,000); the biggest retreat by Pittsburgh (down 167,000).

This was odd, in a way, for by playing around with statistics, one could make out a case for Pittsburgh's being just about the last big city anyone would wish to leave. Among the ten largest S.M.S.A.s in the nation, Pittsburgh had in 1970 the fewest reported burglaries per 100,000 inhabitants (814, as contrasted with, for instance, Detroit's 2,062 or Los Angeles's 2,209), and the fewest reported auto thefts per 100,000 (442, as contrasted with New York's 952 and

[91]

Boston's 1,120).* An explanation for Pittsburgh's relapse emerged, though, when one reflected that economic motives underlie most migrations and one noted that among these ten major communities Pittsburgh, for all the comparative invulnerability to depredations it offered, ranked last in median family income—$9,737 as contrasted with Philadelphia's $10,783 and Chicago's $11,931.

Between 1960 and 1970, the population of the country increased by 13 percent. But the pattern of growth was by no means uniform from coast to coast. The metropolitan areas of the twelve north central states, for instance, had a net increase of 2 million migrants from 1940 to 1960, but in the following decade they stayed just about where they were. Their net population growth of a little under 10 percent in that stretch was entirely the result of more births than deaths. The nine states of the northeast failed, too, to match the national growth rate, also increasing at less than 10 percent. The 13 percent overall average was largely attributable to the performance of the West, which shot up by 24 percent, and in the course of that escalation California found itself, with 19,953,134 people, the most populous state of them all. Sheer momentum would, by mid-1971, propel it into be-

---

* If one correlates the right statistics, one can make a stab at proving almost anything. By putting together various data on illiteracy, television, motels, mobility, fertility, and venereal diseases, one could probably make a persuasive case that, since the introduction of color television into most of the nation's motel rooms, traveling salesmen have got into far less trouble, and have got far fewer girls into trouble, too.

coming the first American state ever to harbor 20 million individuals.

With so many of them around, it would be understandable that, among 2,150,000 permits issued nationally in 1972 for the construction of new housing units, 280,000 were granted in California. It was more significant that 282,000 of these were concurrently handed out in Florida. Los Angeles accounted for 53,000 of them, and its rival-in-size New York for 51,000; but two much smaller communities in Florida were close behind—Miami with 50,000 and the Tampa–St. Petersburg complex with 27,000. The country's newest megalopolis was taking shape along a 100-mile stretch of Florida's east coast, from just above Palm Beach to just below Miami. The three counties in this area—Palm Beach, Broward, and Dale—had among them in 1960 a total population of 1,497,232 and a population density of 284 per square mile. By 1972, they were up to 2,397,789 people and a density of 454.

The California of 1970, now that it had attained primacy, was resting, as it were, on its laurels. That year, for the first time in a century, as many people moved *out* of California as moved into it. To have access the year round to balmy weather was one thing (discounting forest fires, smog, beach pollution, and the possibility that an earthquake might substantially reduce the size of the state and add to the dimensions of the Pacific Ocean), but no matter what the temperature may be anywhere, the lack of a job can make people shiver. In the early 1960s, when the employment picture was sunny in California, the state attracted an average of 1,000 net migrants every day. By 1970, with the national unemployment rate at 6.1 percent, California's was 7.4 percent; and further on up the West Coast, Seattle, with a rate of 9.5 percent, was such a comparative economic wasteland that the Japanese sent it a shipload of relief supplies. Since 1970, California, which throughout the twentieth century has regularly increased its population at at least twice the national growth rate, has barely been holding its own, in percentage terms, with places like North Dakota.

To Northerners accustomed to thinking of the South as a backward region whose Congressional spokesmen exercise unreasonable influence, it is sometimes troubling to be reminded that, whatever the flaws in the seniority system by which committee chairmen are chosen and retain power for life, the South cannot be ignored, if only for the reason that it has more people than any of the other three major regions of the country. (It can also claim, in a sense, to be the most American part of America. Southern hospitality is one thing, but Southern inhospitality to immigrants from abroad is quite another, and it has been consistently manifest; in 1920, for example, when 58.7 percent of the native white population of Rhode Island was of foreign or half-foreign parentage, only 0.64 percent of North Carolina's was; in 1970, the comparable figures for those two states were 32.8 percent and 1.9 percent.) At the time of the 1970 Census, there were roughly 35 million people in the thirteen Western states, 56,500,000 in the twelve North Central states, 49 million in the nine Northeast

states, and 62,000,000 in the sixteen Southern states
—most of them living there because they desired to.
(The Census Bureau ascribes to the Northeast Maine,
New Hampshire, Vermont, Massachusetts, Connecti-
cut, Rhode Island, New York, New Jersey, and
Pennsylvania; to the North Central Ohio, Indiana,
Illinois, Michigan, Wisconsin, Minnesota, Iowa, Mis-
souri, Kansas, Nebraska, and the Dakotas; to the
West Montana, Wyoming, Colorado, Idaho, Utah,
Nevada, Washington, Oregon, California, Arizona,
New Mexico, Alaska, and Hawaii; and to the South
the rest of the States.)

The South's total represented a 14.2 percent net
gain in population since 1960—less of an increase by
far than the West's, but also more by far than the
North Central's or Northeast's. Between 1965 and
1970, the entire Northeast had a net loss in interstate
migration of 722,281 people, the North Central of
615,098. The West gained 694,889 and the South
642,490. Eleven of the twenty-one new Standard
Metropolitan Statistical Areas recognized by the
Bureau of the Census between 1970 and 1972 were in
the South, which by then—its plantation-and-magno-
lia image notwithstanding—had more people living
in central cities, 18,645,558 of them, than any of the
other three regions of the United States.

And despite the monumental outflow of its long-
resident blacks, in 1970 the South still had more of
them—53 percent of all there were—than the rest of
the country put together. In this respect also, though,
there had been singular changes. In 1940, 77 percent

of the nation's blacks lived in the South, and they represented 24 percent of that region's total population. Thirty years afterward, the South had only a bare majority of all blacks, and the ones it had were only 19 percent of its people.

Between 1960 and 1970, every single one of the eleven Confederate states showed a loss in blacks—231,000 for Alabama, 279,000 for Mississippi, and so on. Most of the black males in the South today are either very young or very old, a situation that can hardly be of comfort to black Southern politicians, who are beginning to attain some clout at just the same time that they are sorely lacking what in other areas would normally be considered—whether or not they actually vote—the core of their constituency. Still, the South remains unique in that, despite their depletion, it retains the country's only appreciable number of black people who live outside of metropolitan areas. In 1970, there were 103 counties in the United States at least half black, and every one of them was in the South.

The South led the nation, moreover, in other measurable categories—ones in which its preeminence could have brought it little comfort. It had more of the poor and fewer of the rich, on a proportionate basis, than any other region. In the Northeast, 7.6 percent of all families had incomes below the poverty level; in the North Central, 8.3 percent; in the West, 8.9 percent; in the laggard South, 16.2 percent. Conversely, whereas the Northeast contained 24.4 percent of all families with annual incomes of $15,000 or more, the West 23.8 percent, and the North Central 21.6 percent, the poor South had only 15 percent.

The rural blacks—limited by income and education and isolation—are not likely soon to become significant shapers of national destiny, but their urban brothers and sisters have already become just that. They are becoming so perhaps faster than they could have anticipated, for in a sense they count more than double: For every one of them who has lately moved into a big city, more than one white has moved out. This has been the story not merely in New York but, to name only a few other places, Boston, Cincinnati, Cleveland, Des Moines, Louisville, Minneapolis, Newark, New Orleans, Oakland, Philadelphia, Providence, San Francisco, and St. Louis. In 1970, Detroit, with a total population of 1,513,601, was 43.7 percent black (and it should be borne in mind that all black urban populations are probably higher than the official Census figures). Detroit's total population fell nearly 10 percent from 1960 to 1970; at the same time, its black population rose nearly 40 percent. Baltimore's total went down 3.6 percent, its black total up 29.1 percent.

For those few cities whose overall totals rose, the black totals rose even faster. Dallas had an increase of 24.2 percent and a black increase of 62.7 percent; for San José, it was 118.3 percent and 460.4 percent; for Altadena, 4.5 percent and 674.7 percent. But let us not be carried away by percentages. There were only 42,000 people in Altadena altogether, and the fact that the Appleton–Oshkosh area of Wisconsin showed a 267.9 percent increase in blacks over the decade dwindled in significance when one realized that at the start of the decade the place was 99 percent white. A 500 percent increase of one person could merely signify that he got married and had two children and a mother-in-law in his house.

There are many paradoxes in the North–South relationship. Surely one is that, while statesmen were debating busing, statisticians were determining that, whereas only 27.7 percent of Northern and Western black students attended schools that had a majority of whites enrolled, 38.1 percent of Southern blacks did. It was paradoxical also that while the Southern part of the country was becoming urbanized at twice the speed of the North (of course, it had a lot of catching up to do), and while it had those nearly 19,000,000 central city residents, only 56 percent of its people lived in metropolitan areas. For the rest of the country, it was 69 percent.

All these city folk had to come from somewhere, and they came largely from the farm population, which has fallen off more rapidly and radically than many people are aware. The dwindling of the influence of American farmers probably began during the War of 1812, when the cessation of trade with England induced a flurry of manufacturing in the United States, and the factory hands had to be recruited mainly from among former agricultural workers. Agriculture, of course, remained consequential; even after the Civil War, more than half of all employed persons in the country worked on farms. In 1870, 53 percent of all workers and 58.1 percent of all male workers were engaged in farming. And, as recently as 1920, the nation's population was just about evenly divided between city and country—55 million urban residents, 51,500,000 rural.

By 1970, however, the rural population had scarcely changed; it stood at 53,600,000. (There were rural sections of the country, indeed—southeastern Nebraska, northeastern Kansas, southern Iowa, much of Missouri, northern Tennessee, and others— with counties that had attained their maximum population growth way back in 1900.) At the same time, the urban population had nearly tripled, rising to 149,300,000. In 1920, one in every three Americans was living on a farm; in 1971, one in every twenty-two. The enormous widening of that particular gap becomes graphic when one visualizes a map of those counties that in recent years, despite the national advance, have undergone a loss of 10 percent or more of their population; they cover a broad swath from Texas north through Oklahoma, Kansas, Nebraska, and the Dakotas, and westward to parts of New Mexico, Colorado, and Wyoming, and to most of Montana.

The Dakotas were two of the only three *states* that actually dropped in population between 1960 and 1970. The third was West Virginia (forty-seventh ranking state in median family income in 1969, just ahead of Alabama, Arkansas, and Mississippi), which between 1965 and 1970 had a net out-migration of

185,125 people—11 percent of its 1970 population. Fewer than 250 of West Virginia's army of defectors headed toward either of the Dakotas; 13,515 made it to Florida, and 5,677 to California; but more than half never got beyond the contiguous states of Maryland, Pennsylvania, Ohio, and Virginia.

At the other end of the scale, Nevada led the gainers in population, with a 1960–1970 increase of 71.3 percent. True, it had started from a smallish base, but in the second half of that decade alone interstate migration brought it 110,078 new residents —43,012 of them from California, where the glamour was wearing off and gambling was illegal. Only 23.6 percent of 1970 Nevadans who were native-born Americans were born in Nevada.

Most of the counties that diminished in population were farm counties. In 1970, only 4 percent of all employed men between twenty and twenty-four were engaged in agriculture; by contrast, 12 percent of this age group were working for some government agency—quite a few of them, no doubt, in the Department of Agriculture. The federal government now dispenses about $10 billion annually in benefits of one sort or another to our dwindling farmers, just as if nothing had changed back on the farm. But things have changed, all right. In 1960 the farm population of the country was nearly 16 million. In 1970, just as the total population was for the first time passing the 200 million mark, the farm population for the first time since the 1820s was dipping below 10 million. So, Agriculture had $1,000 or so to spend for every agricultural man, agricultural woman, and agricultural child there was. Meanwhile, Congress was allocating $433 million for environmental quality control, which came to about $2 an American—farm families, of course, included.

In 1850, the nation had 1,450,000 operating farms. By 1935, the number was 6,800,000. That was the peak, and then, as mechanization became widespread and more and more small farms were gobbled up by large ones, the number began to decline, dropping below 3 million, for the first time in more than a century, in 1969. (There were 428,000 fewer farms in 1969 than in 1959, but their average size was thirty-eight acres larger.) Around 1980, demographers surmise, the number of farms will fall to under 2 million.

But even though the farm population has plunged by 38 percent in the last decade alone, we must again look at the figures cautiously. For there remain all told 4,500,000 American farm workers, a larger labor force than the employees of the steel, automobile, and transportation industries together—indeed, if one can call farming an industry, the largest industrial force in the nation. And there remain more than a billion American acres—close to 47 percent of all the land area we have—devoted to farming; 48 million less of them than there were in 1964, but still a fair garden patch.

The efficiency of farm workers, furthermore, has multiplied more splendidly than that of many of their contemporary laborers. In 1820, the average farm employee produced food enough to sustain four people. In 1950, he could feed fifteen; in 1970, forty-five. Although the number of corn-growing farms in Iowa dropped between 1959 and 1969 by nearly forty thousand, the value of the Iowa corn crop rose by $1 billion, and the number of Iowa farmers with annual sales of over $40,000 more than doubled. Pennsylvania counted 2 million fewer farm acres in 1970 than it had had ten years before; no matter, the value of its farm products was up by more than $150 million. And in South Dakota, at the same time that the number of farms was falling from 49,703 to 45,726, the average farm size went up from 916.8 acres to 996, the average value per acre from $61.60 to $83.89, and the total market value of farm products from $629 million to $958 million.

For the nation as a whole, annual sales of farm products rose between 1964 and 1969 from $35,300,000,000 to $45,600,000,000, which, were it not for the existence of the budget of the Department of Defense, would be a formidable figure. (In that sometimes well-rewarded group of farmers were 474 mushroom-growers who among them grossed $59 million, for an average of $124,000 apiece.) South Dakota alone had 4,500 farms with annual sales over $40,000. For American farmers everywhere, annual gross sales rose between 1964 and 1969 from an average of $11,176 to $16,705. The farms that fared the best were the bigger ones; the largest decrease in the number of farms occurred among those whose yearly sales of products were under $2,500.

For all the affluence that he sometimes seems to

harvest, the American farmer is a worthy cause of concern. For one thing, he is, on the average, getting old; too few young people are going into farming to keep the average decently down. The average age of farm proprietors in 1945 was 48.7; in 1971, it was over fifty-one. Of all South Dakota's 45,726 farmers, only 1,250, at last reckoning, were younger than twenty-five; 5,547 were sixty-five or older. In 1970, South Dakota had one of the highest percentages in the country of people over sixty-five still in the labor force—32.4 percent. Probably quite a few of them were men whose sons had failed to stick around to take over from them. The comparable percentage for the country was 24.8. Altogether, in 1970, there were 1,981,379 individuals over sixty-five who were still in the labor force.

After sixty-five, presumably, nobody *wants* to work and everybody wants to have his brittle bones warmed, but not everybody can afford it. Forty-five percent of all people over sixty-five in South Dakota who didn't live with relatives were on welfare. (Only 1,857 South Dakotans of any age made it to Florida between 1965 and 1970, and only 2,126 to Arizona.) By far the largest number of South Dakota's farmers were in the forty-five- to fifty-four-year age bracket. As for the national farm population, in 1960, people fifty-five or older constituted 18 percent of it; in 1970, they were a quarter of it. There was such a departure of young adults of child-bearing age from the nation's farms that the number of farm children under fourteen dropped 50 percent in the decade.

Within the more and more circumscribed agricultural community, massive changes were occurring. Most of the people who continued to work as farmhands no longer lived on farms; that might have been the main reason for their being willing to stay in the vicinity. In the old days, it had been more or less taken for granted that if you lived on a farm, you farmed, and that if you farmed you lived on a farm. But whereas in 1960, 75 percent of the Americans engaged in agriculture actually lived on farms, in 1970 only 63 percent did; the rest had joined the society of commuters. The number of farmers not living on the farms they ran rose from 291,000 in 1964 to 458,000 in 1969. And whereas in 1960 64 percent of those who lived on farms also worked there, a decade later it was only 54 percent; the rest of the farm population—excluding the migrant crop-pickers of the nation—either worked at non-farm occupations or did not work at all, being in many instances, as we have seen, too old to.

VI

☆ ☆ ☆ ☆ ☆ ☆

From Farm to City to Suburb

How the people of the United States have shifted themselves slowly about the continent, like some enormous centipedal creature, can be succinctly summarized: Since 1900, the total population has been multiplied by 2.6, the metropolitan population by four, and the suburban population by six. The excess of production of automobiles over the breeding of horses is one cause. Those who deplore this trend toward clustered and cluttered living, though they can do little more about it now than wring their hands, can draw some comfort from the fact that, while it is still continuing, it is abating. In the 1950s the country grew by 19 percent and its metropolitan components by 27 percent; in the 1960s the metropolitan growth rate of 15 percent was much more nearly in line with the national rate of 13 percent. In any event, one of every four Americans now lives in one of the ten biggest urbanized areas or its immediate environs.

Meanwhile, rural America has come to a bizarre

pass. Were it considered an entity apart, its total acreage would make it the world's ninth biggest land mass. But in terms of income, with the country's unmatched wealth even more concentrated than its citizens, these hinterlands would at the same time be the world's sixth largest underdeveloped nation, backward in income, in housing, and in education, and outstanding only—the plight of many urban residents notwithstanding—in poverty. It was not surprising that the number of incorporated communities in America with a total population of less than twenty-five increased in the 1960s; as the big got bigger, the small got smaller. In 1960, there were seventy-nine of these frail settlements. In 1970, there were 116—fifty-three of them in the increasingly barren no-man's-land from Texas north to the Dakotas. North Dakota alone had seventeen of them. We do not know who lived in these exceptionally tiny hamlets. But we do know something of the makeup of those that, in the American scheme of things, must also be accounted small. In 1970, towns with populations of 10,000 or less had within them only 12 percent of all the people, but they had 26.8 percent of those over sixty-five.

By contrast, the number of American metropolises of more than 100,000 increased over the same period from 130 to 153—from New York to Parma, Ohio. Some of them are more than mere cities; in the view of the Census, the Standard Metropolitan Statistical Area of Washington, D.C., encompasses parts of the states of Maryland and Virginia. Over the 1960–1970 decade, the total number of S.M.S.A.s rose from 212 to 243, and as noted earlier, to 264 subsequently. Ninety-three percent of the population of California, for all its forests, groves, and ranches, lived in 1970 in one S.M.S.A. or another, though some of these areas were metropolitan more in name than nature. The region called the Standard Metropolitan Statistical Area of San Bernardino–Riverside–Ontario covered 27,295 square miles—more than four times the size of Rhode Island. The S.M.S.A. of Jersey City, with nearly the same population as its California country cousin, took in only forty-seven square miles.

Jersey City held the questionable distinction, at last count, of leading all S.M.S.A.s with populations over 200,000 in auto thefts—1,267 yearly per every 100,000 of population. On the other hand, it was rather low in dentists, with only 56.8 per 100,000. Ann Arbor, with 111.5 dentists per 100,000, thoroughly dominated that field, eclipsing even New York City (96 per 100,000), often thought of as a citadel of dentistry. Ann Arbor, curiously, also led in burglaries, with 2,502 per 100,000 (New York: 1,821; Jersey City: 1,038). No particular reflection on dentists is intended.

Some S.M.S.A.s have spread out because cities have annexed abutting areas. Oklahoma City grew over the decade from 215 square miles to 636, the result of having gobbled chunks of five adjacent counties. Various cities and counties have elected to merge, to increase their size, as did the Virginia city of South Norfolk and Norfolk County; from this union evolved the new city of Chesapeake. All the cities of Texas have the right to annex, which was one reason why the metropolitan population of that farflung state went up by 22 percent in ten years. Countrywide, 6,700,000 people lived in 1970 on land that wasn't considered metropolitan in 1960 but has been redefined—most of it land in counties that became parts of S.M.S.A.s when a core city within the new borders passed the 50,000 mark.

So, when we say that Americans are increasingly metropolitan, it doesn't mean that all of them have moved to more crowded areas. It may be that metropolises have moved in on them. There are still a few farmers tilling the soil in what, statistically, is now urban territory. The swing toward metropolitanization stems partly from the desire of many individuals to be involved with big cities and partly from the belief of local governments that assimilation or affiliation can produce economies and efficiencies. Size, though, is no assurance of savings: New York City, the behemoth of the lot, paid more per capita in 1970 for solid waste disposal than any other S.M.S.A. It cost $15.46 a head. Portland, Oregon, performed the same unglamorous, unavoidable service for $1.93.

The core of every S.M.S.A. is its central city—by demographic definition a municipality with a population density of at least 10,000 per square mile. In 1960, the population of the nation was just about equally divided between central cities, metropolitan suburbs, and everyplace else. As the suburbs have flourished, the other two categories have faltered.

There was a total gain of 20 million metropolitan people between 1960 and 1970, but 17 million of them belonged to the suburbs; the central cities barely held their own.

The upshot was a dramatic redistribution for the nation as a whole: 76 million in the suburbs, 64 million in the central cities, 64 million for the nonmetropolitan remainder. Manhattan Island, the hub of New York and in the eyes of the world the epitome of American cityness, lost 9.4 percent of its population during this time of change. Mostly it lost whites—nearly 200,000 of them. More than half of *all* metropolitan whites now live outside of central cities, in pointed contrast to only 20 percent of all metropolitan blacks. Manhattan was 24 percent black in 1970, and New York City as a whole had 1,666,636 blacks—only 21.2 percent of its total population, but at the same time the largest concentration of black people on earth.

Four million of the country's 22,672,570 blacks lived in just four cities: New York, Chicago, Detroit, and Philadelphia. In the 1960s, from all sources (migration and births together), the black and Puerto Rican population of New York rose by about 900,000 (Puerto Ricans are hard to pin down statistically, since many of them quite properly can and do identify themselves as white); these two groups together constituted some 30 percent of the city's total.

By 1975, they will probably constitute a good deal more of the New York City population, whether or

not immigration from other areas continues or
ceases. Fertility will account for it. Even today, only
15 percent of all the children in New York City
public schools are neither black, nor Spanish-speaking, nor Oriental, nor American Indian. Fifteen
percent is an important proportion for New York;
that is also the percentage of its residents who are on
relief. Some say this is a terrible situation in the
showcase city of the nation. Others believe that it is
not without its good points, because the presence of
so many stricken people in an area of such stridence
stamps them on the public consciousness and may
even stir the public conscience. If so large a segment
of the nation's poor were tucked away in Appalachia,
they would be out of sight and out of mind.

The central city of Washington, D.C., was unqiue
in 1960. It was the only big city with a black
majority—54 percent—and, with Charleston, South
Carolina, and Bessemer, Alabama, one of the only
three cities of more than 25,000 with such a majority.
By 1970, Washington was 71 percent black, and it
had been joined by fifteen other cities over 25,000
that had become at least half black. By then, too,
there were three other big ones where the balance
had been tipped: Newark, Atlanta, and Gary, Indiana.

When the nation went to the polls in November
1972, blacks were elected to 1,144 offices, ten times
the number they'd had in 1965, when Congress
passed the Voting Rights Act. If more blacks had
acted upon those rights, black candidates might have

fared even better; while 55 percent of all Americans of voting age cast their ballots for somebody, only 44 percent of black Americans took part in the electoral process. Those who did not could have made a difference. In fifty-eight Congressional Districts, blacks constituted at least 35 percent of the population. Thirty-seven of these districts were in the South, thirteen had populations that were more than 50 percent black, and eleven now have black Representatives in the Capitol.

In that same election, eighty-six blacks were voted into mayors' offices, as opposed to only twenty-nine in 1968. Many small Southern communities, of course, are overwhelmingly black, but only 51 percent of the current crop of black mayors were put into office in the South. Newark and Gary, like Washington, had black mayors, which seemed reasonable enough in a democratic society; Atlanta had a black vice-mayor, which even ten years earlier would have been hard to imagine in Georgia's principal city. Seventy-seven percent of the children in Atlanta's elementary public schools were black. In that year, for the first time, black students outnumbered white students in San Francisco's public schools.

The upward surge in the percentage of blacks in the inner-city part of Washington derived no less from their actual numerical increase of 126,000 than from the concurrent numerical decrease of 136,000 for whites. Thus the nation's capital fittingly reflected a national trend—just about one white person departing from a central city as one black person arrived. The restructuring of racial balance in the District of Columbia had a good many statistical side-effects. With the blacks as a group having more children than their white predecessors, the median age for the city dropped from 32.2 to 28.5; it would have been even lower but for the city's having experienced a deficit of 40,000, between 1960 and 1970, among native whites younger than nineteen. Only 33,000 of this group were left in town; their black age peers numbered 219,000.

In few other ways, however, was Washington representative of the country to which it dictates. Its population density—12,321 per square mile—was uncommonly high. It had a very high death rate and at the same time, in its suburb of Montgomery County, could boast one of the few geographical entities that as early as 1972 attained the goal of Zero Population Growth. It gave one pause that, concurrently, Montgomery enjoyed the highest median family income of any American county with 50,000 or more inhabitants—$16,710. Still another Washington suburb, the unincorporated village of Bethesda, was even more affluent, with a median of $21,116.

In 1970, Washington also had an unusually high proportion of educated residents. Seventy-three percent of its inhabitants twenty-five or over had finished high school, and 40 percent had at least one year of college; for nearby Baltimore, the comparable figures were 44 percent and 16 percent. Washington was thus a fairly clearcut example of the effect—regardless of race—of education upon income. The District's median family income of $12,933, while not a match for the $15,862 of Stamford, Connecticut (a haven, of course, for largely white corporate executives), was more than double the $5,983 of Miami (a haven for retired senior citizens), and nearly three times the $4,776 of McAllen, Texas (a dispatching point for itinerant Mexican-American crop pickers). McAllen's median-income figure, the lowest for any S.M.S.A. with a population of 50,000 or more, correlated neatly with other standard indices of deprivation. Only 30.3 percent of its residents over twenty-five had finished high school (the national metropolitan figure was 55.3 percent), and its cumulative fertility rate for women between thirty-five and forty-four was 4,563 (as against 2,416 for New York City, 2,636 for Los Angeles, and 2,849 for the country as a whole). But correlations can be paradoxical: the Provo–Orem S.M.S.A., in Utah, had led the nation in high-school graduates, with a 72.7 rating, but despite their superior education they were not faring too well economically; 11.7 percent of them were living below the poverty level, as against 8.5 percent for the whole country.

It was the presence of battalions of government employees, of course, that gave Washington its statistical singularity. Nationwide, in 1970, 18 percent of all workers not engaged in agriculture worked for some branch of government. For Washington, the figure was 42.1 percent. (For New York City, it was 16.5 percent; for Houston, 11.9 percent.) Washington had the largest percentage of white-collar workers, most of them federal employees, of any community in the United States—57.9 percent, against the national average of 48.2. Across the country, 80 percent of all federal employees were adjudged white-collar ones; 88 percent of Washington's federal workers made that pristine grade.

The national proportion of bureaucrats in the more rarefied field of public administration was 5.5. percent; Washington's was 27.1. Fifteen percent of the *blacks* employed in Washington held professional, technical, or managerial jobs; in no other quarter of the country did blacks make a comparable showing. Detroit, though, was another place that seemed for many of them worth working in. There, as in Washington, 40 percent of all the resident black families had incomes of $10,000 or more. By contrast, 40 percent of the black families in Birmingham, Jacksonville, Memphis, and New Orleans had incomes below the poverty level.

From 1960 to 1970, there was a slight diminution of the proportion of black families in Washington with incomes under $8,000—a diminution naturally to be welcomed at a time of inflated cost of living— and it was accompanied by a sharp rise of 195.7 percent of families in the over-$15,000 bracket. (In actual numbers, there was less to be excited about: There were 57,123 of the under-$8,000 families and 20,696 of the over-$15,000 ones.) Nonetheless, while between 1965 and 1971 Washingtonian blacks held 15.1 percent of all federal jobs in their region, they occupied only 1.9 percent of the jobs in the three top civil service classifications. They were big frogs only in small ponds.

Eighty-eight percent of Washington's blacks lived in parts of the city that were three quarters black, and only 2 percent in parts that were less than one quarter black. Seven out of every ten of the capital's blacks, moreover, lived in sections of the city that fitted the federal definition of a poverty area; and in these depressed and depressing enclaves nine of every ten residents were black. As the color of Washington's central city markedly darkened, even the Redskins left it to practice in the suburbs.

Some blacks moved out, too—160,000 of them between 1960 and 1970. But most of these actually just spilled over into those suburbs directly abutting their inner-city ghettos. In the remainder of Washington's many suburbs, blacks complained, there simply was no housing that they could afford, assuming they'd be welcome if they had enough money. The only suburb in which blacks have made substantial residential gains, oddly, has been Prince Georges County, Maryland, where the Bureau of the Census, which has over 1,000 black employees, is located.

One result of this state of affairs has been that it is difficult for blacks to work at all conveniently in some of the federal agencies that themselves occupy suburban quarters. Greater Washington has become so diffuse a community—with the Pentagon, the C.I.A., and the Census Bureau itself, among other proliferating arms of government, now outside the

District of Columbia—that only 45 percent of all the jobs it could dispense in 1970 were within its central city, which was where most blacks lived.

This was a fairly recent development. In 1960, there were 483,000 jobs, a preponderance of them governmental, within the city, and 274,000 in the suburbs. In 1970, there were about the same number —492,000—within the city, but there were 597,000 outside of it. Two thirds of New York City's employment opportunities were inside its central city boundaries, and three quarters of Houston's.

How complicated a nation to operate ours has become! By 1970, we had reached the point where to run all our governmental functions, federal, state, and local, seemed to require the employment of 12,320,637 individuals—14 percent of all the country's working males and 19.5 percent of its working females. We got by in 1960 with only 7,859, 997 of them. A decade later, we needed, or at any rate had, 3,284,241 federal employees, 3,016,396 state, and 6,020,000 local.

New York was the only major central city to increase in population between the last two decennial Censuses, and it grew by merely 1 percent. (There was little about its growth to hearten libertarians; in 1970, two thirds of the 2,159 tracts into which the Census Bureau had divided it were either 90 percent black or 90 percent white.) All the other central cities, owing to the surge to the suburbs, backtracked. In 1950, 35 percent of the national population lived in central cities, and 27 percent in the suburbs. Twenty years later, it was 31 percent for the central cities and 37 percent for the suburbs—and this in spite of the physical growth of many cities through annexation.

The shift was not gradual, but rapid and recent. By 1920, only 17 percent of all Americans (18 million, that was) were suburban. By 1930, it was only 19 percent; by 1940, only 20; by 1950, only 24—a mere 7-point change in thirty years. Then the pace quickened: 33 percent by 1960, 37 by 1970. Among whites, it has been a far-reaching dispersion, with blue-collar families heading toward the suburbs at just about the same rate as white-collar ones. It has been an epochal kind of dispersion, too, because, although this was far from the case in 1920, nowadays whenever we allude to "1 percent" of our population we are talking about 2 million human beings.

It used to be that many young married people would move from the central cities to the suburbs when they started to have families, and go back when their children grew up. Statistically, that pattern has vanished. The inconvenience of putting up storm windows notwithstanding, Americans in their fifties have stopped returning to the cities. In Westchester County, New York, sometimes thought to be archetypical of suburbs, nearly all the white population growth in recent years has come from people *over* fifty-four.

The young marrieds may continue to be the stereotypes of that particular suburb, but they no longer accurately characterize it. Of late, indeed, there has been a net statistical loss in Westchester of children under five (part of this no doubt attributable to declining birth rates), and the number of individuals between the ages of five and seventeen has stayed just about the same. The crime rate hasn't, though; as most of our suburbs are becoming more crowded and less elitist, their incidence of violent crimes is increasing at a pace twice that of their nearby big cities.

At the same time, though, that the suburbs *have* been taking on some of the less agreeable aspects of the cities they outlie, they have become startlingly less dependent on them—exchanging their suburbanity for self-sufficiency. Of all the nation's 21,456,444 employed persons who lived in the suburbs in 1970, about 75 percent of them worked in the county of their residence, which meant in most instances that they did *not* travel to the nearest big city to earn their livelihood. The most up-to-date Census figures indicate, furthermore, the extent to which suburban families throughout the country patronize suburban business establishments. Between 1958 and 1967, while the central city rates of growth of employment in wholesale and retail trades were 10.5 percent and 7.7 percent, the comparable suburban rates were 90.2 percent and 60.6 percent. Even in the Northeast, the legendary citadel of the American commuter, where the heaviest concentration of suburban residents exists, 66.2 percent of all workers, wherever they lived, didn't cross a county line to get from their homes to their factories or offices. The commuter is getting to be as antiquated as the train he commutes on.

As the suburbs have waxed, so, perhaps inevitably, has their rusticity waned. The year 1970 was notable for, among other things, being the one in which for the first time in American history the suburbs sneaked past the central cities in the dubious rivalry to see which category could shelter the most people. The score was 23,905,000 housing units for the suburbs to 22,591,000 for the central cities. The explanation was simple: Of the 10,400,000 new housing units constructed in the entire country over the previous decade, 5,500,000 had risen in American suburbs. And 1970 was the year, too, when the traditional horizontality and exclusivity of suburban living were overtaken by the verticality and communality theretofore chiefly associated with the cities. In 1970, Westchester County took a look around and discovered that it had more multifamily housing units than single-family ones.

VII

☆ ☆ ☆ ☆ ☆ ☆

Defusing the Population
Explosion

THE FOURTH OF DECEMBER 1972 COULD TURN OUT to be a milestone date for the United States—a day as historic as the Fourth of July, the birthdate of any President, or the termination date of any war. For that was the day on which it was announced, somewhat to the Census Bureau's surprise, that American women had finally got around to bearing children at a rate below the critical figure of 2.11 per capita and had thus, for the time being at least, transformed their nation into one that had attained a Zero Population Growth rate.

If every man and woman produced exactly enough offspring to replace themselves, the Z.P.G. figure would, of course, be an even "2." The extra eleven-hundredths that statisticians have appended is supposed to allow for those unfortunate females who die before reaching child-bearing age and by so doing throw statistics involving reproduction out of kilter. Consequential as the 2.11 may be to demographers, the figure probably crosses the minds of no more than something like .00211 percent of the women who collectively determine whether or not a society exceeds it, falls below it, or, improbably, hits it right on the mark. On that December fourth, without any particular fanfare from the White House (which was then preoccupied with reducing the population of North Vietnam), American women were found to be having children at the rate of 2.08 apiece. (By March 1973 they were down to 2.03.) Even during the Depression, when there was a marked decline in the size of American families, the rate had never dipped below 2.2. As a result of the startling new low birth rate, the population of the United States increased during 1972 by only 0.7 percent. During the 1960s, the average annual rate of increase had been nearly double that—1.3 percent. So radically had things changed that by 1973 pregnant women were being stared at on city streets; they had become a kind of novelty.

That a falling-off in population is, all things considered, a desideratum for the United States had been argued earlier in 1972 by the ill-fated Presidential Commission on Population Growth and the American Future. This was the group, under the chairmanship of John D. Rockefeller 3rd, whose detailed analyses and recommendations were on the whole ignored by President Nixon, the man who had brought it together in the first place. In its report to the White House, the Commission said that "we have always assumed that progress and 'the good life' are connected with population growth. In fact, population growth has frequently been regarded as a measure of our progress. If that were ever the case, it is not now. There is hardly any social problem confronting this nation whose solution would be easier if our population were larger."*

The assumption that such growth was progressive might have been wrong all along: Those members of our national community whose rate of increase had been the most rapid had seldom shared proportionate to their numbers in the distribution of the resources that are commonly acknowledged to contribute to the good or better life. For instance, in 1970, there were 207,000 families in the country—rather special ones, to be sure, but nonetheless real enough—made up of a single woman and six children under eighteen. These unusually proliferating households had been unusually detached from the good life: 82.5 percent of them were below the poverty level.

The resolute blow struck by American women in 1972 against population growth was received by the Census Bureau with guarded optimism. For all anybody there could tell for certain, the decline in births might prove to be a temporary phenomenon. There were, after all, large numbers of women reaching child-bearing age every day, and they might exercise the option often basely attributed to them of changing their minds.

But the Bureau, though taken aback by the sud-

---

* *Population and the American Future*, Signet Special from the New American Library (New York, 1972) p. 1.

denness of the unprecedented development, had already anticipated that something of the sort was in the wind. In trying to make projections of future population totals—which Census people are always careful to differentiate from *predictions*—its statisticians had been using four arbitrarily selected multiples. As Meyer Zitter, one of the Bureau's principal projectors, remarked in conversation, "We decided a long time ago that you can't reliably predict a change in birth rates. All you can do is show what is likely to happen if people pursue any one of a variety of possible courses. We once used three assumptions—high, medium, and low—but we switched to four because with three, every time we issued a report people would throw away our top and bottom numbers and use the middle one as Gospel. It wasn't that at all, or indeed anything but a reasonably informed speculation; the only thing we're certain of around here is that fertility is always going to fluctuate."

In the fecund 1950s, the actual rate of births per woman in the United States has been 3.51. In 1967, accordingly, the Bureau's projection people chose as their assumed rates 3.35, 3.10, 2.78, and 2.45, the last being the lowest multiplier that anyone deemed plausible. Population projections based on these four variables were issued as Series A, B, C, and D. In terms of what this all meant, if women had averaged 3.35 children apiece throughout the remainder of the twentieth century, the total population of the country by the year 2000 would be (assuming a constant immigration of about 400,000 people a year) 361,000,000; at the 2.45 rate, it would be 260,000,000. The effect on population of women's reproductive caprices can be illustrated in another way: If every potential mother in America produced one extra child between 1970 and 2000, the national total would balloon by 50 million.

By 1970, however, actual births were found to have decreased so rapidly that the Bureau abandoned its Series A—the 3.35 multiplier—as unrealistic, and substituted a Series E. The magic Z.P.G. number of 2.11 was chosen for that one; nobody dreamed that an even lower multiplier might be useful, or necessary. But that a new minimum was required became swiftly apparent. The Taeubers' giant knowledgeable monograph, completed at the end of 1969, referred only to the A, B, C, and D series; by the time it was published, at the end of 1971, not only had A been dropped by the Bureau and E adopted, but B had also been eliminated as unrealistic and still another Series, Series F, unveiled, with a multiplier of a mere 1.8. So now 3.10, a figure well below the actual rate of the fifties, was the greatest multiplier, and the smallest one was substantially below Zero Population Growth.

The Bureau could take this step with at least momentary confidence; for in 1972, even though there were 2 percent *more* women of child-bearing age in the country than there had been the year before, there had been 9 percent *fewer* total births. The difference in population in the year 2000 between the old Series A projection of 3.35 and the new Series F projection of 1.8 would be 110 million. So many million fewer children—and their absence would presumably be unlamented by the mothers who didn't bear them. For the Presidential Commission had also reported that 15 percent of all the children who *had* been born between 1966 and 1970—2,650,000 children—had been unwanted.

As Meyer Zitter and others are always warning, however, fooling around with fertility figures is a slippery science. The men and women born between 1905 and 1915 had got past their child-bearing years with just about reproducing themselves (a depression and a war had been the chief inhibitions); but those born between 1930 and 1935 (postwar adults, breeding in the carefree fifties) had passed the terminal level of the Series A projection—had already had, that was, more than 3,500 children for every thousand couples—at a point when most of the women among them were still in their twenties and still physically capable of considerable further procreation.

In any event, though the rate of Zero Population Growth has now finally been achieved, so large is the number of women now reaching child-bearing age that, even if the rate does not once again increase, we will have to wait for the population to level off until the daughters of the girls now being born complete *their* procreation—roughly seventy years—for the population to stop increasing. And, inasmuch as in 1972 there were 1,900,000 eighteen-year-old women (compared with 1,400,000 in 1962 and 1,000,000 in 1952), half a million contemporary young women could elect never to have a child at all and there would nonetheless be as many potential mothers on tap as there were a decade earlier.

It is moot, then, whether our phenomenally declining birth rate will stay low or will continue in the future, as it has in the past, to fluctuate. What it will do will almost surely be influenced by business conditions; there would appear to be a strong correlation between procreation—as there has been in the case of migration—and the state of the national economy. Hitler tried to get German mothers to breed to furnish him with soldiers, but what actually convinced them that they should go after his baby bonuses, most demographers believe, was the end of post–World War I inflation.

As during the Depression of the 1930s there was a sharp curtailment of births in the United States, so, conversely, have boom times produced baby booms. The greatest number of Americans living in 1970 to have been born in any single twelve-month period were delivered between April 1, 1959, and April 2, 1960. They were conceived when the economy was thriving, and in numbers they are almost double the thirty-six-year-olds who came into the world at the trough of the slump.

There was another spate of breeding right after the Second World War; during the war itself, the national growth rate had been perceptibly slowed by dislocation of families, unavailability of husbands, and doubts about the future. Then servicemen came home, some to their wives and some to get married, and the dormant population tide erupted. In 1970, the postwar babies—those men and women between twenty and twenty-four—numbered 16 million. Another measure of population growth is the national fertility rate—the number of children produced annually per thousand women between fifteen and forty-four, which are the normal child-bearing years. In 1936, the fertility rate slumped, too, down to 75.8; in 1957, a baby-boom year, it reached 122.9; in historic 1972, it hit a rock-bottom 73.4.

The population of the United States has tripled in the twentieth century, going from 76 million to well over 200 million. But while the annual growth rate was 2.3 percent in 1900, by 1970 it had fallen to 1.1 percent. As the surviving children per thousand mothers have dropped from 3,200 to 1,800, moreover, and as improved public and private health programs have pushed life expectancy in America from 1900's forty-seven years to 1970's seventy, we have a much more spread-out population than we ever had before. Our infant-mortality rate is now 19.8 deaths per 1,000 births, nowhere near as good as Sweden's 11.7 per thousand, but more presentable than the Soviet Union's 24.4 and incomparably better than—Dr. Schweitzer's efforts notwithstanding—Gabon's 229.

Today, with better, cheaper, and more readily dispensed contraceptives, and with liberal abortion laws, it is far easier than ever for women to exercise the latent power they have always had—the power to avoid having children. It is interesting to note, in this connection, that a study made outside the Census Bureau in 1970 among married Catholics, those women historically least disposed to alter nature's rhythms, revealed that 68 percent of them in the eighteen- to thirty-nine-year age group were using contraceptives. These were white Catholics who lived with their husbands and who took Communion at least once monthly, and among those of them twenty to twenty-four, the rate was even higher—78 percent of this subgroup electing to ignore the dictates of their church.

The 104,290,000 women of America enumerated in the last big Census may have been put upon in many ways, but they could, accordingly, shape the destiny of their country as no man ever could: they could determine (isolated rapes aside) how many Americans there should be. In a motley nation, one finds an unusual homogeneity of attitude among women against big families; and for all anyone can tell this may be their permanent stance, and business cycles be hanged. For the desire to reduce family sizes has clearly been shared by all fertile women, whatever their region, education, age, race, or color. It may be especially significant that the birth rate for poor women—who with less education and less access to reliable contraceptives and to abortions might be expected to lag behind their better-endowed sisters— has actually been going down the fastest. It declined by 21 percent in the 1960s, while the rate for women above the poverty level was declining by 18 percent.

In absolute terms, if in that decade the country's poorer women had continued to reproduce at their rate for the previous decade, there would by 1970 have been a million more children than there actually were.

The more acquainted that women of all classes become with contraceptives and abortions—and their men folk with vasectomies—the less likely they are to revert to their mothers' and grandmothers' breeding habits. One additional factor that would certainly seem to have influenced the contemporary child-bearers' performance is the new morality, with all the access it offers to frank talk about sexuality. It is hard these days for a young woman to become pregnant by surprise.

As our women have acted—or not acted—in concert, they have already racked up some startling statistical accomplishments. Between 1960 and 1970, the national population of children under five fell by 15 percent, the biggest drop in the nation's history. At the start of that decade, for every thousand women between fifteen and twenty-four there were 1,600 of these young children; at the end of it, only 958. What a statistic like that means is, among other things, thousands of fewer jobs for elementary-school teachers. It could also mean something of a breath-ing-spell for the hard-pressed administrators who make up urban budgets; education is the major item in most state and local governments. (Even with the diminution of youngsters, these governments all together now allocate 40.1 percent of their funds to education, as compared with 11.2 percent for welfare, 7.4 percent for health and hospitals, and 4.7 percent for police.) The relative scarcity of children could even portend a deceleration, not too far away, in our soaring crime rates, inasmuch as half of all the Americans who are arrested for all causes are under twenty-four.

The number of children that women *expect* to have cannot be a firm measurement of anything but their intentions, and any number of variables can raise or dash their hopes. Even so, that statistic shows how the American female mind has been running, and it has clearly been running away from the nursery. In 1955, American women expected to have an average of 3.2 children apiece. By 1967, they were willing to settle for 2.9, in 1971, for 2.4, in 1972, for 2.3. Catholic mothers' expectations dropped between 1966 and 1971 from 3.45 children each to 2.75; the decline in birth expectations for married Catholic women between twenty and twenty-four was twice that for comparable non-Catholics. In Census Bureau surveys among wives of all religious persuasions between eighteen and twenty-four, only 44 percent reported in 1967 that they hoped to have two or fewer children. In 1971, 64 percent of them expressed that hope.

In sum, nearly two thirds of the entire group anticipated reproducing at *below* the Zero Population Growth point. In 1967, only a little over 1 percent of these young married women expected to have no children at all; four years later, nearly 4 percent of them planned to remain childless forever. By the same token, whereas the earlier survey disclosed that nearly 8 percent of the mothers expected five or more children, in the later one less than half that proportion had such great expectations. Those looking forward to four or more went down from 26 percent in 1967 to 12 percent in 1971 and 9 percent in 1972.

Men are not without their own birth expectations. One of the first things a thirty-year-old Air Force captain was quoted as saying after being released from a North Vietnamese prison camp in February 1973 was, "My wife and I had one goal—to have sixteen kids. After that, it doesn't matter." But he had been locked up for five and a half years and hadn't yet had a chance to talk things over with his wife, whose views might have changed in the interim.

Now that American women appear to have decided spontaneously and emphatically to keep their nation's population within manageable bounds, one wonders whether much or any of the rest of the world will keep step. (The United States is, of course, not the leader in this respect; Japan achieved a Zero Population Growth rate in 1957.) What could happen elsewhere on earth if women in this or that nation merely maintained their present reproductive patterns boggles the imagination. Should Brazil, which had a population of 17 million in 1900 and 93 million in 1970, cling to its present rate, by the year 2070 there would be 1.5 billion Brazilians—the equivalent of nearly half the entire global population a century before. This could conceivably happen; in most of

Latin America, only 2.3 percent of all women between fifteen and forty-nine are known to have thus far accepted contraceptives.

The population of Mexico would rise in those hundred years from 50 million to 1,500,000,000, and of Uganda from 10 million to 160 million. (General Idi Amin, the Ugandan chief of state, who is sometimes aptly called Big Daddy, is a Moslem and has four wives, each of whom presented him with a child in a recent single month.) India would overtake China as the world's most populous nation—9 billion to 6 billion. The United States and the Soviet Union would be comparatively small-potatoes countries, with less than a billion inhabitants between them. Already stabilized Japan, its population having levelled off in the year 2030 at about 200 million, would be lost in the human shuffle.

VIII

☆ ☆ ☆ ☆ ☆ ☆

Women and Children Last

Women can govern their fertility in all sorts of positive and negative ways—by, for instance, getting married later than their predecessors or by deferring the time of their first pregnancy. American women have been doing both. Between 1890 and 1960, the average age at their first marriage went down two years; between 1960 and 1970 it rose, from 20.3 to 20.9. Their average age at the birth of their first child went up from 21.8 in 1960 to 22.1 in 1968. (Most marriages still occur in June, and the fewest in February and March, but more American children are nonetheless born in the fall than in any other season.) American women have moved so far from being housewives and mothers that 45 percent of those between 14 and 35 are now single.

The non-marriage rate is slightly higher for the Northeast than for the rest of the country, one reason being that it is statistically harder to find a husband in the Northeast, where in 1970 (if one can believe the Census) there were only 93.3 males for every hundred females, and where 90 percent of all women under twenty-one were single. For the country as a whole, there were 94.8 men then for every hundred women. (Twenty years before that, it had been 98.6 men per hundred, and in the West men actually predominated—102.1 to 100. "Go West, young woman" would still be cogent advice for young females with family aspirations: In that part of the country, men are also in the minority today, but merely by 97.8 to 100.) In 1970, only 64 percent of all women between twenty and twenty-four had ever been married; in 1960, 72 percent of that group had been. Despite all this, 83 percent of all women between the ages of sixteen and seventy in 1970 had been married. There are, proportionately, fewer youthful marriages, but more mature ones; older people less often nowadays have children or grand-children to live with, and they don't much like to live alone. Then, too, of course, there are many contemporary young women who have mates but have not bothered with matrimony. And there are marital freaks among us, furthermore. In 1970, the United States boasted 2,983 very young men who, at the age of fourteen, were already widowers, and 289 even more precocious young women who at that same age had been both widowed *and* divorced.

The Census Bureau, which does not measure affectionateness, suggests strongly that the success of marriage is affected by two factors that are very much its concern—education and income. A June 1971 survey showed that in 90.4 percent of households where the husband and wife were both college graduates (the husbands in this particular inquiry being between thirty-five and fifty-four), each of the partners had been married only once. Such stability was characteristic, though, of only 75 percent of those households where neither partner had finished high school. The survey further indicated that it does not necessarily seem to be true that people get divorced because they can afford to. There had been no more than one marriage in 83 percent of the households with incomes over $15,000; but this was so in only 71.7 percent of those with incomes under $5,000. While the Bureau was thus investigating marriages, it came up with some good tidings for sentimentalists: Of the 48,125,000 married women in America in 1971, 15,900,000 had already celebrated their twenty-fifth wedding anniversary, and 1,200,000 their fiftieth.

As the institution of marriage has, overall, diminished in importance, it has not inevitably followed that America has become a nation in which divorce is rampant; but the old foundations of wedlock have certainly been shaken. Between 1960 and 1972, the annual number of divorces increased by 80 percent. In the mid-1960s there had been 500,000 divorces a year. At that time, and indeed until very recently, most demographers considered the divorce figures for the years just after the Second World War—when hasty wartime marriages were tottering and foundering—to have been phenomenal and unsurpassable; the average annual number from 1945 through 1947 had been 526,000. In 1971, though, that total was spectacularly eclipsed; there were 768,000 divorces. And in 1972 the total went well over the 800,000 mark.

A recent study by Paul C. Glick and Arthur J. Norton, two of the Census Bureau's leading family statistics experts, disclosed that slightly more than one quarter of all married women between twenty-seven and thirty-two can, if the present pattern persists, be expected to get a divorce at some point or other in their later lives, and that about one fifth of these divorcées will remarry and then get a second divorce. (Even so, only about 3 percent of all Americans between the ages of fifty and fifty-five who had ever been married by 1970 had been married as often as three times.) It is difficult for demographers to project or predict divorce rates with any exactitude, because whereas women can be counted on to divulge their birth expectations with reasonable candor, few people are likely to tell an enumerator that they *expect* to get divorced.

Eventually, however, the divorce rate could turn about and start to dwindle, inasmuch as mature individuals get divorced less frequently than younger ones, and as people are marrying at a later age. In 1959, for instance, nine of every thousand single white women got married at fourteen, and thirty-one of every thousand blacks. Of women who marry in their teens, 27 percent get divorced within twenty years; of those who marry in their twenties, only 14 percent do.

For all that women can and do control the nation's population, they remain noticeably behind when it comes to the nation's economy. Women with the same education and job experience as men fall far short of commensurate rewards. A recent Census Bureau survey among women between thirty and forty-four who had worked steadily since leaving school revealed that their median annual income was nearly $3,000 less than that of men with precisely parallel careers. In terms of earned income, women stood worse in relation to men than did blacks to whites. In all job categories, the median earnings of women were less than half those of men, though this discrepancy was somewhat mitigated by the circumstance that far more women than men worked only part-time. For full-time workers, the median income for all men in 1971 was $9,630, and for all women, $5,700. Among all the 10,038,986 white women between thirty-five and fifty-four who were in the labor force in 1970, many of them perforce part-time workers, the median was $4,457; and as we glance from spot to spot that women customarily dominate, we suspect they do not much enjoy that distinction— the 76,439 file clerks averaging $4,130, the 267,500 typists $4,256, the 101,022 textile operatives $4,030, the 652,735 food-service workers $2,422. Let us hope that tips were not included.

The 7,051 female social scientists tabulated averaged $9,347, the 3,933 college administrators $9,488, and the 10,872 computer specialists $9,350; but the 789,039 salesworkers were at $3,313, the 563,466 in

retail sales at $2,915, and the 47,949 gadget-demon-
strators, hucksters, and peddlers—the Avon Lady's
life cannot be all primroses—$1,720. For the 81,049
bank tellers, the figure was $4,282, which these days
will not buy fifty ounces of gold; for 546,388 bookkeepers, $4,766; for 227,451 cashiers, $3,380. In view
of these stipends, that there are not more embezzle-
ments or petty thefts committed by women who
handle money and ledgers is little short of flabber-
gasting.

The situation was not entirely bleak: In 1969, there
were 1,600,000 women who were earning more than
$10,000 a year—seven times as many as there had
been a decade earlier. In 1960, of some 44,000,000
families with both husbands and wives in them, 3.2
percent of the wives had received more income than
their mates; a decade later, 7.4 percent of the wives
had. That came to 3,200,000 wives, 61 percent of
whose husbands were working. More than one million of these women brought in at least $3,000 in
excess of what the head of their family accounted for
(the "head" in these instances seeming to be a very
sexist appellation); when it came to that, there were
380,465 husband–wife families boasting a child who
produced at least $3,000 more than the head himself.

Despite the clear improvement in income of a few
women, the sisterhood in general had little to be
cheerful about. For back in 1955 full-time women
workers had been earning 65 percent of what their
male counterparts received, and fifteen years later
they were getting only 59 percent as much.

It is true, of course, that as long as women continue to bear the primary responsibility for running households, they can anticipate fewer work options. (As of October 1972, only 96,000 men between twenty and sixty-four were regarded by the Census Bureau as "homemakers"; the women so designated numbered 25,300,000.) Women can't, as a rule, work at all hours and thus earn lucrative overtime pay; a husband's income is less affected by a child's sore throat than is his wife's. Even in those fields where women workers predominate, they are discriminated against. Women teachers in 1970—including part-time ones—outnumbered men by more than two to one, but their median pay was less than two thirds of men's. For full-time teachers, the picture was a little brighter, but not much: The women got less than three quarters of what the men got. For factory workers, it was just over half; for retail salesworkers, less than a third.

All in all, however, women have become an increasingly important economic factor, and not because of how they spend their husband's earnings but how they obtain their own. In 1940, only 25 percent of women over fourteen were in the labor force. In 1960, 34 percent were, and in 1970, 47 percent. In March 1970, the American labor force of 85,900,000 included 31,600,000 women—43 percent of all women over sixteen. There were 13,800,000 new jobs in the country during the 1960s; women filled 8,400,000 of them, including 75 percent of the openings for bus drivers. (The average income for a female transport operative in 1970 was $2,309.) And women were getting more of the better jobs. Between 1950 and 1971, the percentage of those who were professional, technical, or kindred workers rose from 9.5 to 16. And over about the same period of time, while the percentage of women employed in manufacturing went down from 33.7 to 26, that of those in government jobs went up from 13.3 to 18.6. Many government jobs are tedious, but probably in most instances it is less disagreeable to shuffle papers than to candle eggs on an assembly line.

Whereas in 1960, moreover, only 31 percent of all married women were in the labor force, a decade afterward 41 percent were. There were 10,200,000 working mothers. More than one third of all women between fifteen and forty-nine who had children under five were engaged in gainful work, and nearly 20 percent of all these women were black. Even one fourth of all women with children under three did some work.

It is easier, nowadays, for women *to* work; with all our technological advances, there are fewer jobs around for which they are ineligible because they lack brute strength. How the nature of women's employment has changed can readily be shown: In 1900, nearly half of all working women were domestic servants or farmhands; in 1960, only one tenth of them were. Today, slightly less than 4 percent of all working women remain in domestic service. The percentages for the South, however, where large household staffs are disappearing less slowly than in other regions, are higher: 9.2 for Alabama, 10.3 for

Mississippi, 10.5 for Louisiana. Texas, though nowhere nearly as populous as California or New York,
has more females thus employed than either of them;
Georgia has more than Pennsylvania, Ohio, or Michigan; Alabama has more than Illinois or New Jersey.

Practically all these Southern servants are black; as
a result, although white women outnumber blacks by
eleven to one, there were almost the same number of
black domestics in the country in 1970 as whites—
519,900 to 533,200. But black women in general
could find some statistical cheer: A decade earlier,
there had been 898,400 of them in domestic service,
and as that number had fallen off sharply since 1960,
so had there been a concurrent increase of black
female clerical workers (from 219,000 to 719,000) and
of black females in professional, technical, or similar
jobs (197,400 to 406,600).

With so many labor-saving devices now in their
homes, women naturally have more *time* to work. (It
is debatable whether these devices make it possible
for women to work or whether women work to make
possible their acquisition of the devices.) The essential point is that more and more women want to
work, quite apart from those who, because of the
ascending cost of living or because of male unemployment, simply have to work to supplement, or
indeed provide, their families' incomes. It would
probably be fair to conclude that if most American
communities were ever furnished with decent day-
care facilities for small children, or if the Women's

Liberation Movement persuaded enough men to share child-tending responsibilities in their homes, the number of able-bodied women in the national labor force would take a startling forward leap. There will certainly be fewer children clutching at their apron strings to hold them back.

IX

☆ ☆ ☆ ☆ ☆ ☆

The Working Man

MEN REMAIN, BY A WIDE MARGIN, AMERICA'S principal income producers. The nation's bacon was brought home in 1970 largely by its 47,730,661 employed males over sixteen. But there have been profound changes—quite apart from the number of individuals involved—in the nature of this work force's employment. In 1870, for instance, the United States had 145,044 blacksmiths and 400 electricians. In 1970, there were 468,459 electricians and 10,227 blacksmiths. The Census Bureau's scrupulous devotion to anonymity obliges it to leave in its statistically churning wake all sorts of teasing flotsam: Of the 249 *female* blacksmiths tracked down in 1970, for example, six were employed in eating and drinking places, and eleven in credit agencies—this last contingent precisely matching the number of lady blacksmiths who were more believably toiling in blast furnaces and steel mills.

If we examine the figures for various categories of workers during the first half of the twentieth century, we find persuasive statistical confirmation for our surmises about how the country has been transformed. Between 1900 and 1950, the total employed population doubled—from 29,030,038 to 58,998,943 —and quite a few employment classifications grew proportionately. The number of funeral directors and embalmers rose from 16,189 to 40,528, of postmasters from 18,806 to 39,427, of lawyers and judges from 107,620 to 183,551—not precisely 100 percent increases, but close enough.

In other categories, though, there were wild fluctuations from the population norm, indicative of changes in demands for goods and services, and of brand-new thresholds massively crossed. Thus, the number of technical engineers rose from 37,540 to 543,057, of accountants and auditors from 22,916 to 390,423, of credit men from 2,000 to 33,876, and of telephone operators from 19,158 to 374,663. By 1970, with dial phones more and more in use, the rate of increase of telephone operators had slackened, but there were still 407,001 of them around, though not necessarily at a moment when anybody needed to get hold of one. (They were also notably young. The median age for all women in the communications industries was 29.7, higher only than the 27 figure of those in air transportation. For *all* working women the median was 39.2; for all working men, 40.2. The lowest median in any category for the male workers was 29.8—service-station attendants.)

But while, between 1900 and 1950, the *telephone* operators grew in numbers from the size of a village to a respectable city, the *telegraph* operators failed by the size of a reinforced army division even to keep pace with themselves; they dwindled from 55,824 to 35,530. There were net losses, similarly, among ships' officers, down from 43,218 to 42,753; among bus and street railway conductors, from 24,037 to 11,615; among transportation baggagemen, from 19,083 to 8,245; and among leather workers, from 15,810 to 7,510. Shoemakers and shoe-repairers (excluding those in factories) dropped from 101,500 to 60,091, as the small shopkeeper fought a losing battle against obsolescence; metal molders, frustrated by automation, fell from 96,620 to 65,113. The number of private live-in laundresses plummeted, from 279,612 to 75,512. By 1970, indeed, these drudges were no longer even granted a separate classification; there were then still 1,109,858 private female household workers, but, with 95 percent of the nation's homes equipped with washing machines, it seemed reasonable to assume that precious few of these factotums were chiefly preoccupied with sinks and washboards.

Just as notable as the shrinkage of farmers in the first half of the century was that of unskilled nonfarm laborers. There had been 3,007,418 of these in 1900. In 1950, the 100 percent increase in the total work force notwithstanding, there were only 3,287,654. Over the following twenty years, the total work force increased by roughly another 20 million, but the unskilled-labor group by merely 143,628. In seventy years, their number had hardly changed, and instead of constituting a bit more than 10 percent of all workers, the unskilled, like the farm laborers, now were down to 4 percent.

As fewer and fewer Americans, moreover, found themselves tied to what are generally considered the worse jobs, more and more had succeeded in obtaining what are generally acknowledged to be among the better ones. The year 1970, in fact, was a watershed in still another sense: For the first time since the country began taking its decennial dimensions, there were more Americans gainfully employed in business and professional services than there were in manufacturing. True, the margin was slim—20,143,525 to 19,864,209—but finally the land that had practically patented the industrial assembly line had got to a point from which, with automation proliferating in every quarter, it seemed unlikely to be budged: There were more people in it providing services than there were producing goods.

At the same time, there were marked changes in the ratios between white-collar and blue-collar workers. If the figurative color of a working person's collar has the importance that has traditionally been ascribed to it, then America had passed another telltale milestone. In 1950, there had been slightly more blue-collar workers than white-collar—23,336,000, approximately, to 22,373,000. By April 1972, the blue-collar labor force had, considering the new size of the total population, hardly gone up at all, only to 27,744,000; but meanwhile the white-collar group had increased at four times the rate of the blue, and in doing so had moved substantially ahead of it, reaching the total of 38,892,000.

Working women have long tended to hold far more white-collar than blue-collar jobs, possibly because of their assumed lack of physical strength. Among employed white women in 1959, 61.1 percent had white-collar jobs and 17.2 percent blue-collar ones. By 1971, the spread had not varied appreciably—64.9 percent and 15.3 percent. The great bulk of blue-collar jobs had perennially been held by men (some of them necessarily of great bulk), and the percentages for employed white *males* were much more revealing of the shift in national work habits. In 1959, 45.5 of them were blue-collar, as opposed to 39.7 percent white-collar. By 1971, as the pendulum of employment was swinging over from manufacturing to services, so were the white-collar white males achieving numerical superiority—albeit frail—over their blue-collar counterparts: 44.6 percent to 43.7. Still another milestone passed in the arduous pursuit of happiness.

It was at the time of the taking of the 1820 Census that the government first became curious about the kind of work its citizenry was engaged in. The enumerators limited themselves that year to inquiring whether Americans were in agriculture, commerce, or manufactures. By 1840, they were asking about seven categories then regarded as paramount—agriculture, of course, and along with it commerce, manufactures and trades, mining, learned professions and engineers, navigation of canals, lakes, and rivers, and, finally, navigation of the ocean. Ten years after that, there were additional refinements: The army (though not the navy) got a listing of its own; and, as a further seeming snub to maritime workers, all navigators were now lumped together, saltwater ones unceremoniously mixed with fresh. Nonagricultural laborers were isolated, as were domestic servants, and among other categories were "law, medicine, and divinity" and "other pursuits requiring education." There was a separate listing for "government and civil service," areas of employment in which, it could be inferred, a lack of education was presumed to be no handicap.

With each new Census, the occupational categories have been jiggled and juggled. The principal questions asked about employment in the course of the taking of the 1970 Census were devised to ascertain the kind of business or industry a person worked in; whether it was manufacturing, wholesale trade, retail trade, or "other"; what kind of work he did there, what were his most important activities or duties, and what was his job title; whether he was working for the government or a private enterprise or was self-employed—and, if he was on his own, whether he was in a business or profession or in farming.

When the answers were in, it was calculated that on April 1, 1970—in addition to the aforementioned 40 million or so individuals in services and manufacturing—there were 12,266,132 in retail trade; 3,099,812 in wholesale trade; 5,107,427 in transportation, communications, and other public utilities;

4,634,065 in construction; 4,215,525 in public administration; and 4,918,213 self-employed. In agriculture,
forestry, fisheries, and mining—those traditional,
wrestling-with-nature, American pursuits whose early
practitioners will no doubt be much honored when
the nation celebrates its bicentennial in 1976—there
were altogether only 3,503,936 people (in addition to
the "self-employed" in that category). They were
overshadowed, numerically, by the 3,852,540 engaged
in finance, insurance, and real estate.

There are ten major fields of endeavor that the
contemporary Census Bureau considers occupationally consequential: professional, technical, and kindred workers ("kindred" being a member of the
Bureau's terminological family almost as beloved as
"other"); managers and administrators (not counting
those in farming); salesworkers; clerical and kindred
workers; craftsmen and kindred workers; transport
equipment operatives; other operatives; farm workers; other laborers; and service workers (with, in the
case of women, an extra category for private household workers).

Among the nation's working women, the most
densely populated occupational categories were secretaries (2,642,576), salesworkers (2,141,600), elemen-
tary- and secondary-school teachers (1,936,646), and
bookkeepers (1,273,708). More than one third of all
employed women were classified as clerical or kindred.

In the case of men, the big groups were salaried
managers and administrators (3,716,865), saleswork-

ers (3,303,774), construction craftsmen (2,775,378), mechanics and repairmen (2,409,844), salesmen and clerks (2,318,423), foremen (1,444,526), and truck drivers (1,369,678). Truck drivers, as is well known, are the hard core of the Teamsters Union; if that organization had had to rely on Census-tabulated teamsters for its muscle, it would probably not have got as far as it has, for the Bureau tells us that our 1970 total of *them* came to a puny 7,138, and they don't even rate as transport equipment operatives but, rather, as ordinary nonfarm laborers.

Within each of the ten big occupational categories there are—farm workers excepted—multiple subcategories, such as teamsters: fork-lift and tow-motor operatives being one subdivision of the transport equipment group (in 1970, the country harbored 214,062 fork-lift and tow-motor folk, 3,842 of them women); filers, polishers, sanders, and buffers coming under the broader operatives' umbrella (here women played a larger role, accounting for 23,665 of the total of 124,173).

In all, there were, in the Bureau's 1970 view, 441 distinct occupational fields worth isolating. This number, too, has varied from decade to decade. The 1970 total, while considerably above 1960's 297, was no match for 1920's 572. There is a good deal of arbitrariness in the selection of these lower-level occupational labels. Between 1960 and 1970, for instance, the Bureau decided—conceivably at the behest of the Department of Justice—that lawyers and judges, who had long been conjoined, should be set apart. Despite this commendable recognition of a conflict of interests, at the same time other groups of workers whose concerns are not always identical remained firmly yoked—editors and writers, for example, who are sometimes thought to be as hard to count together as apples and oranges. There were, in 1970, 146,925 of both working for salaries or wages, but probably only their publishers, who did not merit a separate listing, knew how many of each.

College presidents rated a special mention in 1960, but they were dropped in 1970, along with baby-sitters and porters—the latter having been split up among "cleaners and charwomen," "baggage porters and bellhops," and "vehicle washers and equipment cleaners." There had been two kinds of baby-sitters itemized in 1960—live-in and live-out. The designation may have been thought to be infra dig; at any rate, in 1970 they all became known as "child-care workers." If men eventually replace women as homemakers, the Bureau, for all anybody can tell, may confer on the baby-sitters an even higher-sounding appellation—perhaps "fathers' helpers."

As the sitters vanished titularly from the Census in 1970, computer specialists made their debut—a stalwart 254,537 of them, so many of them indeed that even at the instant of their appearance they were awarded three subdivisions: computer programers (161,337), computer systems analysts (79,949), and computer specialists "not elsewhere classified" (13,251). These computer people were young. Their median age was 30.8, compared with 38 for physical scientists and 40.1 for engineers. There were by then, moreover, so many Americans employed in welfare services—343,148 of them—that they were removed from "public administration" and listed by themselves. The ranks of government workers had by then grown so huge that the defection could hardly have been noticed. By 1970, one of every 200 living Americans was working for the federal government alone.

But there remained plenty of the rest of us: 56,214 architects (1,981 of them women), 188,769 bartenders (39,381 women), 34,034 bookbinders (19,441 women), 3,659 bootblacks (389 women), 88,448 bulldozer operators (1,135 women), 218,067 clergymen (6,237 women), 5,950 dancers (4,878 women), 166,110 dishwashers (63,991 women), 57,208 earth drillers (3,405 women), 356,660 file clerks (292,252 women), 551,592 insurance salesmen (82,039 women), 121,852 librarians (99,851 women), 675 midwives (138, surprisingly, men), 87,834 musicians and composers (31,493 women), 61,622 newsboys (10,093 women), 11,260 paperhangers (1,111 women), 375,494 policemen and detectives (13,098 women), 73,744 public-relations and publicity men (19,376 women), 24,707 sailors and deckhands (466 women), 97,279 stock-and-bond salesmen (8,880 women), 201,945 tool-and-die makers (4,191 women), and 18,450 veterinarians (985 women).

And although the term "baby-sitter" is no longer in good Census Bureau standing, one is startled to find still in use "hucksters and peddlers." The 1970 head count for this anachronistic-sounding calling came to 117,562, with women markedly predominating— 93,064 of them to 24,498 men. It may have come as a relief to the advertising business to perceive that not a single huckster of either sex was allocated to its rolls, though nine female hucksters and peddlers were credited with performing their unique services on behalf of the trucking industry. To a somewhat allied occupational classification with a classier name— "demonstrators"—3,392 men and 34,462 women were further assigned, and five of *those* women were somehow doing their demonstrating for sawmills and millwork companies.

Any census is at best an imperfect mirror of the society it aspires to describe, and our big decennial ones have hardly seemed to recognize the existence of the big corporations that bestride the American economic scene, and of the big executives that bestride *them*. With its emphasis on poverty and people living in that unhappy condition, the Census gives us look after look at the valleys of our economy; we get few peeks at our peaks. Accordingly, while we know from other sources that there are a few business executives among us with annual salaries of more than $800,000, let alone their other income (45 percent of all American families, incidentally, have no income at all aside from wages and salaries), and, while we know that they are financially significant, we find them statistically invisible.

Indeed, the Census tells us very little at all about our much-envied managerial class, except to suggest, by resorting to averaging, that it is over-envied. There were 6,386,977 managerial types in 1970, among them 1,061,076 women. But that total included funeral directors, school administrators, mail superintendents, building superintendents, railroad conductors, ships' pursers, cafeteria managers, and others who were unlikely to have spent much of their gainful time in corporate board rooms.

The presence in the managerial roster of all these no doubt worthy but hardly manipulative folk (there was no such subcategory as "executive vice-presidents of companies with annual sales of at least $1 billion") helped explain why the mean earnings for all males in this group ended up at only $13,256, a dollar a year *less* than the mean for all civil engineers. The earnings of a lot of cafeteria managers must have been blended with those of General Motors vice-presidents. The average for salaried managers in the motor-vehicle industry, with a good many junior managers clearly included, was a mere $18,488; it was eclipsed by the average for lawyers working for automobile companies, who came in at $30,695. Lawyers employed by finance and real-estate companies, excluding banks and insurance companies, stood at $29,446. The highest average for any managerial employees in these same finance and real-estate outfits was $19,054.

But we are dealing in these two instances with a mere 1,612 lawyers. Doctors are something else again. In fact, any one perusing Census Bureau findings and forgetting to keep reminding himself that corporation executives are swallowed up in them might jump to the conclusion that physicians have the highest earned incomes of *all* Americans. Of course, it may be that they do.

No one could derive greater pleasure from sustained reading of Census figures on incomes than the proverbial mothers of doctor sons. The 1970 mean income for all male doctors over sixteen (and it is hard to visualize any younger than that) was $29,665, more than triple the national average for everybody. (For female doctors, it was $11,150, more than double the average for all women.) The very worst-off doctors, in dollars and cents, were those 1,086 who had somehow ended up in retail trade; they averaged $12,669. (The average for all males in retail trade was $6,838.) The 2,710 doctors in public administration averaged $17,979, the 3,238 in private education $21,418, the 1,403 in manufacturing $24,466. But most of the nation's 254,854 doctors (including osteopaths) were in "other health services," chiefly private practice, and *their* individual mean was $35,866, about three and one half times the average for all American *families.*

Doctors, naturally, have to spend far longer in school than most people before they can begin to earn anything; in 1970, they had just about four years' more education apiece than computer specialists, whose 1970 mean earnings, in the case of the men among them, were $11,004. On the other hand, male elementary and high-school teachers, whose educational experience fell almost exactly halfway between that of the doctors and of the computer specialists, were down at a relatively bleak $8,713, not too far above truck drivers.

The corporation executives, if they cared to, could derive some slight comfort from all these findings. Pulled down as they might have been by the saloon-keepers and others with whom they were statistically paired in the broad managerial category, they could reflect that the doctors' similar category, the pro-fessional-technical-and-kindred one, was similarly affected by the presence in it of the legions of teachers, dieticians, librarians, and writers with whom *they* were bracketed. In one sense, the manag-ers ended up on top after all, for their big occupa-tional group led all the others in 1970 in mean earnings for men, with $13,262, followed by the professionals and their kindred spirits, at $12,262; salesworkers, at $9,875; clerical and kindred workers, at $7,235; transportation equipment operatives, at $7,001; other operatives, at $6,632; service workers, at $5,365; farm workers, at $5,182; and other labor-ers, at $4,913.

And there was yet another soothing disclosure in 1970 for the managerial class. For just as saleswork-ers in the 1960s had edged ahead of craftsmen and kindred workers in mean earnings, so in that convul-sive decade had the managers, a galling second in the 1960 Census to the professional-and-technical frater-nity, finally clawed their way to the top of the occupational heap.

The great majority of the breadwinners in America in 1970 were white males between thirty-five and fifty-four—18,562,369 of them altogether in the civilian labor force. Let us pause and see what kind of bread they won. *Their* average was $10,710. In this age and race group, the 122,240 physicians, preeminent as ever, stood at $37,552, and indeed their extended family—the professional-and-technical people—was actually ahead of the managerial group, by $15,260 to $14,817. (The golden years for managers evidently start a little later.) The average for 116,750 bank officers and financial managers was $16,006. There was very nearly the same number of lawyers (judges here included) in that age group—117,114 of *them*—but there was no similarity in income figures; the legal crowd averaged $27,804.

What should one dream of becoming in his conceivably most lucrative years, those from thirty-five to fifty-four? We are not given breakdowns, during that chronological span, for the comparative achievements of butchers, bakers, and candlestick makers, but we have 1970 figures for quite a few of their cohorts in other fields of endeavor. The 341,970 auto mechanics who qualified had average earnings of $8,032; the 54,100 barbers, $7,046; the 6,552 bank tellers, $7,937; the 386,000 carpenters, $8,025; the 99,559 clergymen, $7,456 (they presumably felt from the outset that their real rewards lay elsewhere than on earth); the 145,237 college and university teachers, $15,198; the 10,387 demonstrators, hucksters, and peddlers, $9,561. The 886 of this last group who finished college, however, did much better, with an average of $16,044.

For the 27,206 economists in this sector of the economy, the figure was $17,649. For the 27,492 editors and reporters (division of the spoils un-known), $14,438; for the 41,422 engineers, $16,312; for the 574,702 farmers and farm managers, $7,436; for the 89,390 firemen, $10,713; for the 12,303 geologists, $16,369; for the 191,901 insurance men, $13,702; for the 128,479 mail carriers, $8,344; for the 96,520 postal clerks, $8,668 (sitting down indoors beat walking outdoors by $324, but may have been less conducive to good health); for the 5,160 radio and television announcers (Walter Cronkite was over fifty-four), $14,201; for the 81,203 real-estate men, $14,513; and for the 599,832 truck drivers, $8,541.

The average for Teamsters Union officials of comparable age was not disclosed, but we do know that the 61,971 bus drivers at that stage of life averaged $7,612, and the 173,966 plumbers $10,107. One can understand from this why so many bus drivers seem crochety—good heavens, they were paid only a trifle more than ministers—but one is at the same time puzzled: Where in the world did all the money go that was spent on plumbing bills? Are the really affluent plumbers those under thirty-five and over fifty-four? Or, bowing to the Census, should the rest of the body politic apologize to plumbers for all those jokes about their wealth?

We have observed that doctors work (though not,

by their yardsticks, conspicuously rewardingly) in retail stores; we can also learn from the Census that an astonishing number of individuals appear to be square pegs in round holes, or round pegs in square ones. Take the offices of physicians throughout the country in 1970 and see who was employed in them. The private medical business was a substantial one, with a total of 416,850 individuals involved—117,650 men, 299,200 women. The numbers that follow are relatively small, but the categories are beguiling. The doctors employed 138 embalmers. (We shall hear more later of *them*.) Five of the embalmers were women. When it came to hiring lawyers, the doctors seemed less open-minded; all of the 125 attorneys working in doctors' offices were male.

Considering the doctors' king-of-the-walk financial standing, it is perhaps surprising that they had no more than 578 accountants working for them full-time (327 of these were women), but what are we to make of some of the other specialists on their staffs? Their 101 credit men and credit women, for instance, their nine athletes, their 219 clergymen (all, like their lawyers, male), their thirteen bakers, fifty-two carpenters, and six tailors? Their 15,601 bookkeepers make sense, but what of their 459 legal secretaries—almost four per lawyer? With doctors' incomes so comparatively high, we can comprehend why their staffs might have included twenty-two economists and eleven airline hostesses, but seven railroad switchmen? Six female foresters and conservationists? Four female fishermen and oystermen? Occasionally, the

Census seems to provoke more questions than it provides answers.

But then perhaps we should reflect that the diversity and variety of American life—the chief corporate manifestation of which must surely be the conglomerate—demands a fusion of our many skills and trades. And there is of course also the matter of job openings; people often have to take what they can get. For otherwise we probably would not find our physicists and astronomers—21,075 males and 866 females—as widely scattered as they are. In 1970, thirty-eight of *them* were working in physicians' offices.

Most physicists and astronomers, to be sure, were doing about what we would expect them to be doing—2,895 in colleges and universities, 4,356 in miscellaneous professional and related services, 4,662 in public administration, 5,945 in manufacturing. Yet there remained five of them in the apparel-and-accessories business, eleven working for retail gas stations, six (all of them male) in beauty shops, six in drugstores, five in real estate, and five in advertising —a sphere of activity that, while it sheltered not a single huckster, could boast its quota of agricultural scientists, ships' officers, surveyors, road-machine operators, and meat-cutters and butchers.

And so it went with one occupational area after another. To mine coal in America in 1970 required (or at any rate had) the services of, among other non-diggers, five optometrists, five furriers, six dental laboratory technicians, and thirty-four fishermen and oystermen. Among the 343,148 bureaucrats who kept the nation's welfare-service offices functioning (the jobs they had may not have been what they were trained for, but were preferable to applying for welfare themselves) were ninety bartenders (fifteen of them women), eight airline stewardesses (four of them men), five petroleum engineers, 1,231 public-relations men and publicity writers, and nine demonstrators. So by 1970 we were publicizing and demonstrating welfare; by the time of the 1980 Census, we may be huckstering and peddling it.

There were also forty-three shoe-repair men and fifteen bootblacks on the welfare-service agency payrolls, but no podiatrists. Six of these, however, were to be found working for religious organizations, only three fewer than the number of foot doctors employed by all the nation's shoestores. The religious organizations also had on their premises a handful of mechanical engineers, boilermakers, furriers, and jewelers, not to mention 307 social scientists; the shoestores among them employed eight barbers, five lumbermen, raftsmen, and woodchoppers, twenty-three painters and sculptors, and, one noted almost with relief, 80,650 shoe clerks.

As for those wide-ranging podiatrists—5,566 males and 460 females all told—they were to be found almost wherever one turned, in electrical machinery, in non-electrical machinery, in grain mills, in yard, thread, and fabric mills, in real estate, in primary

aluminum industries, and in chiropractors' offices.
Four of the podiatrists worked for dentists. What an
inspired time-saving combination!

The military–industrial complex cannot be all
powerful. Even with Richard Nixon in the White
House, it apparently couldn't control the government. For otherwise, in a more than five-hundred-
page Census Bureau publication devoted entirely to
occupations and industries, would not someone influential have insisted on a reshuffling of the order of
three trades cited under "technicians, except health,
and engineering and science"? No such insistence
apparently having been forthcoming, the Bureau,
which was probably too concerned with alphabetical
orderliness to stop and think about ghoulish coinci-
dences, throughout the tome has "embalmers" firmly
sandwiched between "airplane pilots" and "radio
operators and air traffic controllers."

Of our 4,747 embalmers (221 of them women),
forty-three were employed by manufacturing industries, but none in aircraft manufacturing; twenty
were in transportation, but all of these in trucking
services and warehousing. (However, the air transport industry did have in its ranks five female funeral
directors.) Most of the embalmers, of course, were
engaged in personal services—4,035 of them—but
there were also 330 in the insurance business, along
with the previously mentioned 138 in physicians'
offices; and there were another sixteen in newspaper
publishing and printing, five in eating-and-drinking

establishments, four in furniture stores, six in dress-
making shops, and six (all female) in "miscellaneous
entertainment and recreation services." What can
this last mean: that with pornography now so run-
of-the-mill, we are heading toward an era of necro-
philia?

Embalming would seem to be a thriving art.
Nearly one fourth of its practitioners in 1970 were
between sixteen and twenty-four. (Three hundred
and sixteen of the embalmers still on active duty were
over sixty-five.) For all embalmers, the average
number of school years completed came to 13.5—a
bit below the airplane pilots' 13.9, but well above the
air-traffic controllers' and radio operators' 12.4. In
terms of educational attainment, embalmers ranked
almost precisely halfway between newsboys and
chemical engineers. In terms of income, the embalmers were far from the meatiest part of the statistical-
table sandwich in which the Census had them
pinioned. The mean earnings of all of them, including
the 540 of them who were self-employed, were a mere
$7,957, in contrast to $10,593 for the air-traffic
controllers and $18,902—one of the country's highest
averages—for the pilots.

In the entire United States in 1970, there were
49,694 male pilots, and 710 female ones. By now it
does not faze us to learn that ten of them were
working for street railways and bus lines, 231 for
trucking services, thirty for gas stations, and fifteen
for fuel-and-ice dealers. The average earnings for
those pilots actually in air transportation was

$20,859, and for the 28,477 white male pilots between thirty-five and fifty-four, $22,603. And for those between fifty-five and sixty-four—an airplane pilot being a person whose seniority benefits him as much as his customers—the average was $24,059, which put the pilots almost in an income class with dentists.

When one bears in mind that nobody got around to tabulating computer specialists all by themselves until 1970, it is interesting to note that the pilots (at first fancily called "aviators") have enjoyed their own exclusivity since the 1920 Census. At that time, there were just 1,312 of them. That same decennial enumeration revealed the existence in the American labor force of 109,899 locomotive engineers. By 1970, locomotive engineers were by no means extinct, but their number had tumbled to 49,340; for the first time in *their* history, they were, compared to airline pilots, a minority group. Of these surviving train pilots, 392 were women. None of these were working in physicians' offices in 1970, but five female locomotive firemen were. Whoever they were and whatever their duties might have been, in view of the state of health of the nation's railroads, they were probably blessing their lucky stars to be where they were.

X

☆ ☆ ☆ ☆ ☆ ☆

The Foreign Stock

W<small>E HAVE SEEN HOW BIRTHS DECLINED SHARPLY</small> during the Depression, when America was transformed from a land of milk and honey to one of cut-rate apples. There was a concurrent marked dropoff, in those harsh years, of our other recurrent principal source of population growth—immigration. The decade that started in 1931 was the only one after 1820, when the United States more or less began compiling immigration statistics, during which there were more known departures of both immigrant and non-immigrant aliens from our shores than there were arrivals. Over that ten-year stretch, the non-native population of the country showed a net loss of 94,148 people.

It was during that decade, as Albert Speer observes somewhere in his memoirs, that Adolf Hitler expressed the view that "In general, no such thing as an American people existed as a unit; they were nothing but a mass of immigrants from many nations and races." Hitler presumably judged this to be indicative of American weakness. As he was remiss in other respects, so may he have neglected to reflect that the American mass had long been exceptionally Teutonic. For many decades, there had been more immigrants from Germany than from any other foreign nation, and in 1971 there were more Americans of German origin than of any other except English; of those Americans whose foreign roots, if not allegiances, could be discerned, 5 million stemmed from Poland, 8,700,000 from Italy, 9,000,000 from Spain or its former possessions, 16,300,000 from Ireland, 31,000,000 from Great Britain, and 25,600,000 from Germany.

Immigrants are still a consequential element of the American body politic, though in numbers they are less visible than they used to be. In 1850, 11.5 percent of the American population was foreign born, and by 1890 the proportion had risen to 16.6 percent, where it more or less remained until 1910. Between 1901 and 1910, we welcomed, or at any rate received, 8,795,000 new immigrants, a group equivalent to 8.3 percent of the total 1900 population. The net immigration between 1960 and 1970 came to only 3,500,000 immigrants—1.9 percent of the 1960 population. All told, between 1820 and 1971, more than 45,000,000 aliens elected to make America their home.

In 1870, when the United States population was put at 39,818,449, the 5,567,229 immigrants within it constituted 15 percent of the total. One hundred years later, the 9,619,000 immigrants constituted only

4.7 percent. Between 1861 and 1900, they arrived at an average rate of 7.5 of them for every 1,000 of the population; between 1911 and 1970, the average rate dropped to 2.3 per 1,000. As their volume changed, so did their characteristics. At the start of the twentieth century, 80 percent of all immigrants were between fifteen and forty-four; now, only 62 percent of them are that young.

And until 1930, there had always been among them more males than females; many men would come over to make enough money to send for their families or fiancées. More than 80 percent of all our immigrants back in the 1820s were males, and as late as 1920 we took in 150 of them for every female. The proportions varied considerably from country to country. In 1920, for instance, for every 100 Greek women who arrived, there were 443.6 Greek men; Bulgarian men outnumbered *their* women by nearly ten to one. The principal exception to the general trend was Ireland. Largely because of the availability, at cheap wages, of Irish servant girls, in that same year only 78.3 Irishmen arrived for every hundred of their countrywomen.

At the turn of the century, 26 percent of the male immigrants were laborers, and only 1 percent professionals. (Today, only 4 percent of the male newcomers are laborers, and 10 percent are professionals.) But by 1930 the demand for unskilled foreign labor, which had brought so many solitary men across the seas, began to abate; our immigrants tended to turn up in family groups rather than as individuals. Women forged ahead, and they have been ahead ever since. They would outnumber men even more than they do were it not for the recent modifications of our immigration laws, which have resulted in, among other things, a comparatively massive injection into the national bloodstream of immigrants from Asia, whence about twice as many males as females have been emigrating.

The early immigrants, Mexicans and Canadians excepted, arrived by ship, and they were prone to settle near their ports of entry. They had, after all, no automobiles to move easily around in; they stayed near the big coastal ports out of pure inertia or lack of funds to go anywhere else. Even today, migrants leaving the South for the North end up where they do partly because of transportation schedules; it is hard to get off a moving bus. Canadians and Mexicans did not drift far from their first border crossings, either; most Americans of French-Canadian stock live in New England; most Mexican-Americans in the Southwest.

A good many Scandinavians, taking the shorter northern route across the Atlantic, debarked at Canadian ports, and ended up accordingly in our North Central states. Most immigrants wanted to go where they would feel least ill at ease, so they flocked, naturally enough, to where their compatriots had settled—Italians to Rhode Island, Connecticut, New York, and New Jersey; Yugoslavs to Ohio; Danes to Utah; Finns to Minnesota, Michigan, and Oregon;

Norwegians to Minnesota, Wisconsin, and the Dakotas; Irish to New York and Massachusetts.

Few of them from anywhere headed toward the
South, which with a large resident supply of black
labor had little to offer them and moreover didn't
look kindly on folks with strange dialects and ac-
cents. As a result, while the South in 1970 boasted
62,795,367 of the total American population, the
largest number of any of our four regions, and 31
percent of the national total, there were among them
only 4,100,000 people of foreign stock (that is,
immigrants and first-generation natives of foreign or
mixed parentage)—the fewest of any region. And the
majority of these drifted in from nearby Mexico and
Cuba.

In the entire South, only 2.1 percent of the
population was foreign-born; in the Northeast, 8.4
percent. One quarter of the residents of Rhode Island
and Massachusetts were of foreign or mixed parentage, only one hundredth of those of Mississippi.
Among Standard Metropolitan Statistical Areas,
New York was 24.2 percent foreign stock, Chicago
18.4 percent, and Jersey City 24.5 percent; Birming-
ham was 2.2 percent; Chattanooga, 1.3 percent; and
Albany, Georgia, 1.8 percent. The English language
was the mother tongue of 82.1 percent of the whole
population, but of 93.7 percent of that of the four
eastern south central states (Alabama, Arkansas,
Louisiana, and Mississippi), and of 94.3 percent of all
Alabamians.

Some immigrants have moved around, of course, just like native-born Americans, but at a less rapid pace. In 1920, for example, at a time when only about half the native population was urban, three quarters of our foreign-born population was living in cities. By 1950, when 65 percent of our native whites were urban, 84 percent of our foreign-born were. In 1970, the foreign-stock population comprised 21 percent of the population of all our Standard Metropolitan Statistical Areas of 200,000 or more. But these hyphenated Americans behave in large measure like any others. Between 1960 and 1970, New York City lost 150,000 of them to its suburbs. At last count, nonwhites narrowly outnumbered whites of foreign stock within that city—2,925,429 to 2,388,989.

Our immigrants have also traditionally congregated, logically enough, where they could find employment—the mining areas of Pennsylvania and the Western mountain states, the grape-growing valleys of California and New York, the steel mills of the mid-Atlantic states. Many of the earlier immigrants had been farmers at home, but aside from the Scandinavians they did not much gravitate toward the American agricultural states; they had had their fill of tilling the land, and they wanted to be on the barricades during the industrial revolution. So the Poles and Hungarians headed for Pennsylvania's coal mines, the Russians for New Jersey's textile mills, the Greeks to New England, where Greek restaurants proliferated. The impact of the aliens on the nineteenth-century American economy was enormous. In 1870, there were 12,505,923 individuals in the country categorized as gainful workers, and 2,703,889 of them were foreign born.

Of these, only 619,108 were in agriculture—and America was then still very much a nation of farmers; 328,585 were in trade and transportation, 828,615 in professional and personal services, and 929,581 in manufacturing, mining, and mechanical industries. Given the figure of "100" as the norm for employment of all people in all fields, the foreign-born then reached only fifty in agriculture. Among actors, however, Englishmen stood at 472, and Germans rated, not surprisingly, at 901 among brewers. *En masse,* though, the immigrants often came to find themselves doing the most hazardous work, and suffering more than the normal share of traumatic deaths. In 1920, for instance, when the rate of death from lung tuberculosis for the children of native-born mothers in New York City was 77.2 per 100,000, for children of Irish-born mothers it was 183.9.

In every decade of our nation's history from 1810 on, our population increased more from natural births than from immigration. But it must be remembered that most of our immigrants have been young and fertile, and that, as soon as they settled in the United States and had children of their own, their offspring became part not of the immigrant population but of the native-born. So in this statistical sense at least the country has genuinely been a melting pot.

A native American could be psychologically and culturally and linguistically an Iranian or Indonesian, but that was not how he was counted.

Nonetheless, our immigrant population has been giant. From 1890 to 1920, foreign-born people constituted nearly 40 percent of our white population. By 1930 there were still so many immigrants around that half of all of them had been in residence for twenty-four years or more; their median stay of residence was thus *higher* than that of native American whites, whose median age that year happened to be just twenty-four. By 1950, the median *age* of foreign-born whites in the United States, which had been thirty-seven in 1890, had climbed to fifty-six. So comparatively few younger immigrants were then arriving that more than a quarter of all foreign-born residents of the country were over sixty-five.

Now, though, with immigrants comprising less than 5 percent of our population, we are coming closer than ever to being a nation that is 100 percent American, though we are as unlikely to achieve that end statistically as we are ideologically. Interestingly enough, among our 9,600,000 aliens are 253,458 black aliens, and there are an additional 240,471 blacks of foreign or mixed parentage. The bulk of them have come from the West Indies and Latin America, but in 1970 the nation could also claim 42,773 who were born on other foreign soil—among these, 496 blacks from France, 427 from Poland, 374 from Ireland, 338 from Greece, 196 from the Netherlands, and eight from Switzerland. Somewhere in the United States—

confidentiality precludes the Census Bureau from pinpointing their location—are five Hungarian-born blacks now living on an American farm. And on still another farm are six individuals—as beguiling a kind of American family as one could ask for—who are of Spanish heritage and also claim Russian as their mother tongue.

There has been precious little immigration from the Soviet Union since 1930, but "Russians" stand out prominently in many a Census Bureau survey. The reason is that the Bureau, edgy since 1936 about anything with religious connotations, has never been able to figure out a comfortable way of dealing with Jews, and a lot of them who certainly do not think of themselves as Russian end up in that category willy-nilly. Thus in many Census reports "Russians" turn out to be an unusual minority group. In explaining once why 52 percent of all Americans between twenty-five and thirty-four of "Russian" origin had finished college—followed, in rapidly declining proportions, by people with English, German, Irish, and Polish backgrounds, and, at a lowly 1.6 percent, by Mexican-Americans—the Bureau stated, "It is likely that most persons of Russian origin had a Jewish cultural heritage."

There were only 2,200,000 individuals of Russian heritage in America in 1970, but "Russians" stood preeminent on many a chart and graph. Thus, 69 percent of all "Russian"-Americans—roughly translatable as "Jews"—had finished high school, as compared with 55 percent of all Americans. Among the population between twenty-five and thirty-four years old—all of it born since immigration from the Soviet Union had virtually come to a halt—98 percent of the "Russians" had completed high school, as compared with 77 percent for the country as a whole.

They no longer enjoy that academic preeminence. In 1970, among nineteen-year-olds—that being the age when most people decide either to continue their education or go to work—72.5 percent of the "Russian" males and 66 percent of the females were staying in school. The comparable figures for those with Japanese backgrounds were 72.2 and 71.7 percent; and for those of Chinese origin 84.3 and 77.3 percent. For all nineteen-year-old Americans, it was 47 percent.

Although there was no official count of immigrants before 1850, it was not for want of trying. When the United States was coming into existence, the American Philosophical Society (through its spokesman, Thomas Jefferson) and the Connecticut Academy of Arts and Sciences (through Timothy Dwight) both urged the fledgling Congress to include both immigrants and natives of foreign origin in the enumerations it decreed. But even in a young country the legislature moved arteriosclerotically; it waited more than half a century to act on the suggestion. It did pass a law in 1819 requiring the masters of incoming vessels to give to Customs the names and national origins of all their passengers, including those—such were the rigors of travel at the time—who had died en route.

But this was at best an imprecise means of measurement. So it is largely an informed guess to state, as is now generally stated, that between 1820 and 1971 slightly more than 45,500,000 immigrants arrived in the United States. This averages out to 300,000 a year, not far from the current annual in-migration. The biggest years were from 1903 through 1914, when a reasonably reliably enumerated total of 11,791,856 people arrived—an annual average of just under a million for those busy years. The busiest year was 1907, when 1,285,349 foreign settlers arrived.

Eighty percent of all our immigrants for all time have come from Europe. It would be logical to expect that predominant among the foreign-born would have been English, Irish, Welsh, and Scotch persons (along with non–French-speaking Canadians), inasmuch as they were culturally and linguistically the most compatible with native Americans. Notwithstanding, in 1920, just after immigration attained its probably never-to-be-regained heights, four fifths of the foreign-born population of the United States were from *non*–English-speaking countries. This majority may not have had much compatibility, at first, but it had a strong motivation to leave its ancestral territory. And its disadvantages were in many instances swiftly overcome; in the 1920s, 52.4 percent of the male doctors in the United States were of Italian or Russian or (the word was then in the Census vocabulary) Hebrew origin; and so were 17.9 percent of the female schoolteachers.

In the wave of immigration that rippled across the Atlantic between 1820 and 1920, there were various swells of movement from one European nation or another. The big year for the Scandinavian countries was 1882, with 105,326 arrivals. Great Britain's top year was 1888, with 108,692; Russia's 1913, with 291,040 (including a few individuals from the Baltic Provinces, now the Baltic States of the Soviet Union). Poland scored highest in 1921, with 95,089; a hundred years earlier, when there had been 9,127 immigrants from the entire world, just one had been a Pole.

But as far as immigration was concerned the Big Four powers—we are not here counting neighbors Canada and Mexico—were Germany, Ireland, Great Britain, and Italy. At the time the 1970 Census was taken, of the 9,600,000 immigrants officially in the United States, 1,008,533 were from Italy, 832,965 from Germany, and—its recent immigration having been reduced to a trickle—251,375 from Ireland. (A few other totals: the United Kingdom, 686,099; France, 105,385; Yugoslavia, 153,745; Sweden, 127,070; Japan, 120,235.) Of the official total of 45,533,116 immigrants who arrived from 1920 through 1971, Germany has been credited with 6,925,736, Italy with 5,199,304, Great Britain with 4,804,520, and Ireland with 4,715,041. The Irish were ahead of all other nations until 1850, when the

Germans caught up with them. In 1891, Italy passed Germany, but Germany came back strongly in 1931, and stayed ahead of the pack until 1968, when the whole immigration picture was radically altered to the disadvantage, in numerical terms, of northern and to the advantage of southern Europe.

Thus, while in Boston there are now substantially more people of Irish ancestry than of Italian, there are substantially more who were *born* in Italy than were born in Ireland. And New Bedford, Massachusetts, a longtime haven for Portuguese immigrants, has had such a robust recent influx of them (15,959 of its 1970 population of 152,642 either came from Portugal or had at least one parent from there) that aspirants to political office in that vicinity have lately been taking Portuguese lessons and making dutiful pilgrimages to Lisbon and the Azores.

Ireland, as previously noted, is the only place that has consistently sent more women than men to the United States, and its heavy immigration years correlated to the household-worker situation in America. How that situation has changed! Whereas in 1912, some 20,000 young Irish women came to this country to go into domestic service, in 1971, only 10,586 private household workers of both sexes arrived; 3,802 of this number came from the West Indies, and only forty-eight from Ireland. In the United States today, a mere 3.6 percent of all women of Irish birth or descent are employed as domestics—

a bit below the national average, for all women, of 3.9 percent. Irish maids may soon disappear entirely from the American consciousness except when Patsy Kelly is playing them on the stage.

XI

☆ ☆ ☆ ☆ ☆ ☆

*Give Me Your Huddled and
Your Poor—Up to a Point*

By NO MEANS ALL THE IMMIGRANTS WHO CAME TO the United States stayed on permanently, though that was presumably the initial intention of most of them. So, to arrive at net immigration figures, one should subtract from the known immigrant totals the known alien emigrants—who are generally defined as foreigners who after a year or more's residence in America have departed for good. Until 1957, the Immigration & Naturalization Service kept a rough count of emigrants, but then it stopped. It had its hands full keeping tabs on individual border crossings into the United States, which in the fiscal year of 1971 reached the staggering number of 237,557,274. (Quite a few people were counted far more than once; 147,754,249 of the border crossings were from Mexico and 72,610,668 from Canada.) Knowledgeable officials of the Census Bureau have speculated that perhaps as many as one third of all immigrants to the United States in the past century eventually went back home, some having made enough money

to retire on ancestral soil, some out of disenchant-
ment, some doubtless for other good or bad reasons.

But emigration was an area that, largely through
oversight, the Bureau had never explored in depth. In
1969, a young statistician named Robert Warren,
after a brief fling as a left-handed knuckleballer with
the Chicago White Sox, joined the Bureau and was
assigned to make population estimates. The three
main factors to consider, he was advised, were births,
deaths, and immigration. That sounded bush-league
to Warren; what about *emigration,* he demanded.
Nobody had thought much about it. The Bureau has
been trying ever since to come up with some relevant
figures, and has concluded that between 1960 and
1970 there were in all probably 255,000 emigrants. So
now, in issuing figures on immigration, it subtracts
25,000 a year from its totals.

The onset of the First World War marked the
beginning of the end of large-scale foreign immigration to the United States. Nonetheless, so many
aliens had arrived in the years just before then that
by 1920 immigrants and their children constituted 20
percent of the American population of voting age. In
1924, the American Congress, reacting to national
apprehensions about anarchists and other conceiv-
able alien troublemakers, tightened the laws on
admissibility. Some were already restrictive; Chinese
had been almost totally excluded since 1882. (Had we
not barred all but a comparative handful of Asians
for so many years, who can say how differently we
might have approached the wars in Korea and

Indo-China?) The Immigration Act of 1924 stipulated that the future flow of aliens into the country should be consistent with the ethnic pattern disclosed by the 1890 Census. Inasmuch as in the preceding century the great majority of all immigrants had come from northern Europe, that region was heavily favored. We have had quota systems ever since, mitigated by exceptions granted to political refugees, 944,841 of whom were admitted between 1946 and 1971, including 163,493 from Poland, 150,881 from Cuba (in addition to other Cubans in other categories), and 100,181 from Germany.

The immigration statutes were modified periodically after 1924. Up to 1929, for instance, each foreign country was allowed a quota representing 2 percent of its nationals who were inhabitants of the United States in 1890. In 1929, the formula was changed. The overall total was to consist of one sixth of 1 percent of the white inhabitants of the continental United States according to the 1920 Census (after subtracting the number of immigrants and their descendants from Western Hemisphere nations). The country-by-country breakdown was described in officialese jargon, in an annual report of the Immigration and Naturalization Service, as follows: "The annual quota for any nationality for each fiscal year is the number which bears the same ratio to 150,000 [in theory, the total quota] as the number of inhabitants in continental United States in 1920 having that national origin bears to the number of inhabitants in continental United States in 1920, but the minimum quota for any nationality is 100." The immigration laws were further refined from time to time, but until 1965 the 1924 quota system was the basic statute. The quota sometimes fell short of being filled (during the Depression and war years) and was sometimes considerably exceeded (when the postwar refugees were admitted). A characteristic year was 1952, when 11.9 percent of all immigrants to the States came from Great Britain, 60.9 percent from Germany, 23.4 percent from Italy, and .04 percent from all of Asia and all of Africa together.

The 1965 law, which became operative on July 1, 1968, drastically changed the pattern of immigration. Between 1945 and the passage of the new legislation, Europe had been the source of 45 percent of all immigration to the States. Now, the Western Hemisphere was allotted 120,000 places and the entire Eastern Hemisphere—Europe, Africa and Asia altogether—170,000, on a first-come, first-served basis, with a maximum of 20,000 for any single country. There were certain preferences for already resident aliens, for close relatives of American citizens, and for individuals with special skills. By 1970, immigration from all places had increased by 20 percent, but northern Europe's had *decreased* by 64.5 percent. The United Kingdom had been the departure point in 1965 for 27,000 immigrants; in 1970, for only 14,000. Germany dropped concurrently from 24,000 to 10,000. As immigration from Northern Europe slumped, the Southern European totals jumped upward—for Portugal from 2,000 to 13,000, for Greece from 3,000 to 16,000, for Italy, from 11,000 to 25,000, for Yugoslavia from 3,000 to 9,000. Romania seemed singularly unaffected by the new order of things: in 1965, it had sent over 1,644 immigrants, and in 1971, 1,643.

The most dramatic effect of the new law was on Asia. In 1965, less than one tenth of all immigrants came from that continent, but five years afterward one quarter did. The number of nonwhite immigrants from everywhere on earth had been 132,000 in the 1950s; the 1960s produced 524,000 of them, and 1971 an additional 103,461. Asians had been allowed in during the 1950s at an average rate of 15,000 a year; 1970 alone produced 90,000 of them. Immigration from the Philippines increased between 1965 and 1970 from 2,545 to 25,417; Chinese immigration from 2,627 to 16,274. (The Census Bureau arbitrarily lumps together mainland China and Taiwan; statistically minded people are indifferent to the fierce nuances of political and ideological conflict.) Among foreign constituencies in America, the Chinese are— except for the Cubans—unique; there are more of them on hand today who were born abroad than who were born here of Chinese parents. Among all other foreign-stock groups, the children of immigrants now outnumber the immigrants themselves.

One result of the 1965 law was that New York City, which has been losing so many residents of other kinds, experienced between 1950 and 1970 an increase, in its foreign-born Asian population, from 31,977 to 177,906. Still another result of the post-1968

pattern of immigration has been a notable restructuring of New York City's foreign-stock population,
which in 1970 was a group 3,306,000 strong. Whereas
in 1960 the city's foreign-stock constituency was 90
percent European in origin, by 1970 so many immigrants had arrived from the Caribbean islands and
from Latin America that the European proportion
had shrunk to 76 percent. And among residents of
the city who were actually born abroad, the largest of
all groups—larger even than the theretofore predominant Italian immigrants—were the 258,356 people,
half of them black, from the Western Hemisphere.
Today, one tenth of all blacks in New York are
foreign-born.

Our contemporary immigrants from Europe still
largely put down roots where their ancestors did.
More than 4 million of the nearly 10 million foreign-
born inhabitants of the country live in the Northeast.
There are more people of French origin in the
Northeast than in any other region, and twice as
many of Italian origin there as in all the rest of the
country; similarly, close to half of the nation's people
of German origin can still be found in the North
Central states. There have been some changes in
migratory habits, though. Minnesota was the traditional landing place of most Norwegians, and it still
has more second-generation Norwegian-Americans
than any other state. New York, though, has the most
first-generation Norwegians. New York leads, too, in
Czechoslovakian and French immigrants; Pennsylva-

nia has the most second-generation Czechs, and California the most second-generation French.

Most of the newcomers from Asia have elected to settle in California and the other Western states, which, although they now have only 17 percent of the total white population and 8 percent of the black, have far and away the most residents who are neither white nor black—81 percent of the Japanese, 73 percent of the Filipinos, 56 percent of the Chinese, 50 percent of the American Indians, and 51 percent of all the rest.

The number of blue-collar workers among recent immigrants is statistically insignificant—only 18 percent of them in 1971, a far cry from the nineteenth century. In 1971, for instance, the immigrant group included only 1,406 waiters and waitresses and 2,729 cooks (not to mention sixty-four midwives), but there were 4,076 accountants and auditors, 5,756 physicians and surgeons, and 8,987 engineers. More than 60 percent of the professional people who arrived were Asian, among them some 3,000 physicians. There are now 7,000 Filipino doctors in the United States—a number that takes on added significance in view of the fact that the entire complement of black American physicians in 1970 was only about 6,000.

At present, our average annual immigration of almost 400,000 people amounts to just about 20 percent of our net increase in population. (Of course, our *natural* increase has been declining; if and when we reach the day when births and deaths exactly balance, a solitary immigrant would represent 100 percent of our net increase.) We have been dealing all along, however, with *legal* immigrants, and we must pause to take cognizance of the *illegal* ones—precise numbers unknown—who are also very much among us. There were 15,309 bona fide immigrants from Jamaica in 1970, and there are perhaps now 40,000 altogether who enjoy the status of legal resident aliens; some observers of the immigrant scene suspect that ten times that many Jamaicans now live in New York City alone. Between 1962 and 1971, a total of 103,695 Dominicans and 43,956 Haitians were legally admitted. There are probably substantially greater numbers of both around.

The great bulk of illegal immigrants in the country, though, are, as they have long been, Mexicans. Of 317,822 known deportable aliens who were flushed by the Immigration & Naturalization Service in 1971, 313,792 had crossed the Mexican border. More than 120,000 Mexicans are now deported every year, but probably at least one third as many aren't. Many American businesses that can hire them at less than the going wage scale are not minded to report their presence. The Census Bureau has no way of tabulating them, inasmuch as these folk are not likely to identify themselves as having no right to be within its bailiwick; accordingly it must fall back again on guesses as to their numbers. Its most recent guess—throwing in the children born to illegal Mexican aliens who have escaped detection—was between 1 million and 1,500,000. But no matter; the United

States has an amazingly absorptive capacity. And not even taking into consideration those aliens whose entry has been achieved beyond the law, the flow of outlanders into America continues to be, if somewhat diminished, so varied and unending that the country seems in no danger, unless the regulations that govern them become severely restrictive, of losing its rich, strong, foreign flavor.

XII

★ ★ ★ ★ ★ ★

Se Habla Español

Between 1930 and 1970, the largest proportionate growth in urbanization for any ethnic component of the United States occurred not, as one might think offhand, among blacks, but among American Indians. In 1930, 10 percent of the Indians lived in metropolitan areas. Forty years later, 45 percent did. As national groups go, there were not many of them—only 763,594 in 1970, or a mere four tenths of 1 percent of the population. Asked by enumerators in 1970 what tribe they belonged to, 96,743 identified themselves as Navajos, 66,150 as Cherokees, 41,946 as Chippewas, 5,055 as Seminoles, and 3,815 as Utes. It may have been indicative of a broadening of outlook on the part of our oldest indigenes that 20 percent of them professed to have no tribal affiliations at all.

More than half of our Indians continue to dwell in the regions with which they are historically associated; there were still nearly 100,000 of them—Cherokees predominating—in Oklahoma. But 340,000 have migrated to metropolitan areas; sixty American cities now contain at least 1,000 Indians apiece. And these totals are likely to increase, inasmuch as the Indian population—all fantasies about the vanishing red man to the contrary—has lately been growing at four times the national rate. In the 1960s, while the national population increased by 13 percent, the American Indian population increased by 51 percent. Part of this acceleration may have been simply the result of more efficient enumeration; it was often harder to count Indians on reservations than in cities. They weren't counted separately at all until 1890, long after Hungarians and Pacific Islanders had been statistically segregated.

Improved health was undoubtedly another factor; while the current average Indian life expectancy of forty-six is twenty-three years below the national norm, and while the Indian suicide rate is twice that of all other Americans, the Indian infant-mortality rate fell between 1955 and 1971 from 62.5 to 23.8 per thousand; and the death rate from tuberculosis dropped by 86 percent. From 1950 to 1970, the official Indian population more than doubled, and if by any chance it should keep on doubling every two decades at the same time that all other Americans are edging toward Zero Population Growth, by the year 3000 or so there would be 100 million Indians around—conceivably enough of them to try to take the country back.

By that time, however, if the Indians also follow their current mating habits, they should be hard to

identify. Over one third of them now marry non-Indians. The number of Indian women married to
non-Indians doubled between 1960 and 1970. In thus
crossing ethnic lines, the Indians have markedly
departed from the practice of most other ethnic
groups in the nation. There is surprisingly little
intermarriage among the majority of such groups.
Studies made in recent years by Dr. Paul Glick, the
Census Bureau's family man, have revealed that
among major ethnic groups the lines are crossed in
only about seven tenths of 1 percent of all marriages,
and that one fifth of these intermarriages occur
between blacks and whites.

But whereas 33.4 percent of Indian men now have
white wives, only 2.1 percent of black men do. At last
report, there were 23,566 white husbands with black
wives, a slight dropoff since 1960, and 41,223 black
husbands with white wives, a substantial increase but
still, of course, a fairly small number. Half these
couples were living in the South. (In much of the
South, interracial marriage is illegal, but the Census
Bureau makes no distinction between authorized
marriages and the common-law variety.) Three in
every five of these Southern mixed marriages involved a white husband and a black wife. In the rest
of the country, the reverse held true; 60 percent
involved a black husband and a white wife.

There were 55,300 white men who had non-white
wives categorized by the Bureau as "other"—that is,
Orientals, Polynesians, and Indians. Only 34,800
white women had "other" husbands—a tiny drop in

the population bucket. Quite a few of our mixed marriages stemmed from the assignment abroad of so many members of the armed forces; there were just about the same number of Japanese women in the United States married to black Americans as there were to white ones. Dr. Glick has also reported that while Abie's Irish Rose is certainly possible in real life, she is statistically implausible. While 6.8 percent of all Americans identifiable as Jews marry non-Jews, only 1.1 percent of all American women of known Irish backgrounds marry men with known Jewish backgrounds.

The makeup of the United States has been most markedly affected in recent years by those 9,200,000 individuals who, for want of a better all-inclusive term, are generally described as "Spanish-speaking" or as "of Spanish heritage." One of the difficulties of assimilating them into the body politic (assuming that assimilation is desirable) is that, while there were 37 million Americans in 1970 for whom some language other than English was their mother tongue in childhood, the Spanish-speaking tended more than most of the others to cling to the language of their forebears. More than four fifths of the foreign-born Spanish-speakers in the country still used Spanish at home, and nearly two thirds of the *native-born* Spanish-heritage group still used it. In New York City, Eastern Airlines, which runs a great many flights to Puerto Rico and other points south with Iberian overtones, has a special phone number for callers who speak only Spanish.

Se Habla Español

The 4,533,000 Mexican-Americans officially in residence have more easily, or more willingly, adapted to their linguistic environment. Slightly more than half of them speak English wherever they are. But then they have been around longer—in some instances longer than anybody except the Indians. They arrived at Santa Fe in 1609, and they presently constitute 40 percent of the total population of New Mexico. By American criteria, they are astonishingly fecund. In 1970, only 2 percent of all American families had six children or more; 8 percent of Mexican-American families had broods that large. They had so many younger children that, although the median age for all white Americans was 28.6, for all blacks 21.2, and for all Spanish-speakers 20.7, for the Mexican group it was 17.8. Because 48.7 percent of the 1970 population of Laredo, Texas, was of foreign stock, and because 90 percent of the foreign-stock population was Mexican-American, Laredo ended up with the highest birth rate in the country— 42.1 per thousand.

Alas, as they led all others in births, so did the Mexicans trail all others in education. Only 1,000 of the Census Bureau's 2,200,000 "Russians" had had less than eight years of education; 131,000 of the Mexican-Americans had stopped short of high school. The average number of children born to every "Russian" woman at latest reckoning was 2.39; to every Mexican, 4.4.. Only 8.6 percent of all American families had four or more children, but this was the case in 19 percent of all Spanish-heritage families and in 23.5 percent of the Mexican ones. Another way of looking at this: Less than 1 percent of the relatively erudite "Russian" families consisted of as many as eight persons; almost 10 percent of the Mexican-American families (and 7 percent of *all* Spanish-origin families) were that large.

The experience of no other ethnic group in the country suggests as strongly as the Mexicans' that the better an education people receive the less likely they are to conceive. When one further jointly examines the "Russian" group and the Spanish-origin group, further depressing contrasts emerge. Among the former who were employed, 55.3 percent were professional, technical, or kindred workers, and only 6.2 percent laborers or service workers. Among the latter (and in the case of the Mexican-Americans, the spread was even wider), only 13.3 percent were in the two more esteemed categories, but 24.5 percent were in the lower-level ones.

Twenty-eight percent of all Mexican-Americans lived below the poverty level. Compared to their pauperism, the nation's 1,429,396 Puerto Ricans who were officially tabulated in 1970, and who are rarely thought of as prosperous, looked like princes. There were 2,000 Puerto Rican families in the $15,000-and-up income bracket and 1,400 families in the $1,000-and-down. Only 1,600 Mexican families made the higher category—Super-Mex Lee Trevino was in a class by himself—but 3,300 landed in the lower one. (Of all American families, 7.3 percent had incomes above $25,000; of all Spanish-speaking families, slightly beneath 1 percent; of all Mexican families, a puny one half of 1 percent.) Most of the Mexicans lived in the Southwest; as a result, people of Spanish heritage comprised one third of all the poverty population of New Mexico and Texas and one fourth of the poverty population of Arizona and Colorado.

Only in 1970 did the Bureau, taking advantage of the surge of ethnic pride that had begun to crop up in the sixties among blacks, Indians, and other groups, begin asking Americans of Spanish origin to identify themselves as such. Prior to that it had rather haphazardly based its opinion of who or what they were on the look of their name or the sound of their voice. Asking a Mexican-American, for instance, where he had been born, or for his parents' place of birth, wasn't a particularly rewarding avenue of inquiry; some Mexican-American families had been living in what is now the United States for fifteen or twenty generations.

Today, the Bureau doggedly tries to sort out the Spanish-speaking inhabitants of the country, with as much assistance as it can persuade them to render, as Mexicans, Cubans, Puerto Ricans, Central Americans, South Americans, or "other Spanish." After collating the replies to a number of questions— Where was somebody born?, Where were his father and mother born?, Did he have a Spanish-like surname?, What language was spoken in his home when he was a child?, and, finally, Did he consider himself to fit into any other of the Spanish-heritage categories, including "Other"?—the Bureau concluded that in 1971 there were roughly 9,200,000 people legally in the country for whom Spanish had been the mother tongue.

All of these people with some sort of Spanish connection amounted to a bit less than 5 percent of the total population. No fewer than 2,400,000 of them were living in poverty; their median income was $7,550—far below the white median. It would appear to be a tribute to the durability of American race prejudice, however, that although there was a demonstrable correlation between education and income, and that, although our Spanish-speaking residents were by and large less well educated than our blacks (of the former between twenty-five and twenty-nine, only 48 percent had finished high school, whereas 58 percent of comparable blacks had), and although the Spanish-speakers had language handicaps not shared by most blacks—despite all that, the median annual income for the Spanish group was over $1,000 higher than the black median.

Of the 1,429,396 Puerto Ricans whom the Bureau recognized as having been around in 1970, in the spring of 1972 it tentatively allotted 811,843 to New York City, where everybody agrees the majority of the Puerto Ricans live who don't live in Puerto Rico. Almost at once the Bureau found itself again in conflict on a familiar, though not especially agreeable, battleground—the old undercount controversy. Members of the New York Puerto Rican community, with Congressman Herman Badillo leading them in full battle panoply, challenged the figures in every language that came to hand. Badillo demanded a recount, which at last report he had not got, of the South Bronx, where many of his most impoverished constituents resided.

One of the arguments advanced by the Puerto Rican doubters of the count—and it had a persuasive ring to it—focused on New York City school enrollment figures. The Census Bureau had put the 1970 total for blacks in New York City at 1,665,000, this argument went. Very well; that meant there was an official two-to-one ratio in favor of blacks. But if that was so, the argument continued, then how come the school figures showed blacks ahead of Puerto Ricans by merely three-to-two? Did any one seriously contend that Puerto Ricans had *that* many more children per capita than blacks did? It was hard for the Bureau to respond with conviction or passion, since in its previously and often expressed view there had almost surely been an undercount of Puerto Ricans in New York, as well as of blacks; perhaps it all boiled down to a question of how many members of each group had ducked the enumerators. But in this instance, the Bureau observed privately (for federal agencies are wary what they say publicly to or about Congressmen) that there might have been a considerable number of individuals around whom politicians might label Puerto Rican, but who themselves—even though they might have a Puerto Rican ancestor or two—would and could quite truthfully tell a census-taker that they were nothing more nor less than true-blue American.

Being full-fledged Americans, Puerto Ricans do not, of course, have to concern themselves with immigration quotas. This circumstance has recently worked to the advantage of nobody knows how many Dominicans. Dominicans very much resemble Puerto Ricans physically. One can easily travel as a tourist from Santo Domingo to San Juan, and then move along to the American mainland in the guise of a migratory Puerto Rican. Dominican women, several years back, used to go to Puerto Rico and get jobs as domestic servants; there was quite a demand for them, because Puerto Rican women, whatever their impecuniousness, consider it infra dig to do any other woman's housework.

But then the Puerto Rico authorities clamped down on these Dominicans, so Puerto Rican women resumed doing their own chores, and many of the suddenly unemployed Dominicans betook themselves, one way or another, to New York. In the 1950s, 456,000 genuine Puerto Ricans came to the mainland from their island. But relatively few of those crowded in New York did especially well; their median income (the national medians notwithstanding) was consistently a shade below the median of blacks, and almost laughable compared to that of whites. In the 1960s, emigration from Puerto Rico to the mainland totaled only 152,000. By 1970, while it was bad enough that 20 percent of all black families in New York lived in poverty, it was worse that 30 percent of their Puerto Rican neighbors were in that sorry fix.

However unrewarding life might be for some Puerto Ricans in Puerto Rico, at least it was warm there. And however much a shortage of jobs might exist there, in the chilly and unreceptive north the Puerto Rican unemployment rate was 6.7 percent, more than twice that for whites and substantially higher than the blacks'. One of every nine Puerto Ricans in Puerto Rico was on relief; in New York City, it was just about one of every two. In 1960, there had been more Puerto Rican women in Puerto Rico receiving aid for dependent children than there were in New York; by 1970, New York had three times as many of them as their home island. And, while in that decade Puerto Rico's total expenditures for welfare went down, New York's went up by 242 percent. It was not merely the Puerto Ricans, of course, who were accountable for this jump, but they had become a built-in, largely urban minority group of considerable consequence. In 1970, there were 15,000 of them in Washington, D.C., alone.

Still another Spanish-speaking group of recent mounting significance are the Cubans. The Bureau found 544,600 of them in 1970, three and a half times their 1960 total; and, inevitably, there were Cubans in residence who considered *that* tally a gross understatement, perhaps by more than 10 percent. However many Cubans may have migrated northward in recent years—most of them anti-Castro, or at any rate non-Castro—the bulk of them have settled in Florida. Dade County, which consists in large measure of Miami, had almost a quarter of a million of them. In one statistical respect, the Cubans were thoroughly unlike the other Spanish-speakers: The Cubans' 34.1-year median age invested them with an unusual collective maturity.

XIII

★ ☆ ☆ ☆ ☆ ☆

The Race Gap

In an unbiased sort of way, the Census Bureau is one of the most race-conscious institutions functioning in the country. Nearly all its findings are uncompromisingly broken down in terms of black and white. (It is one of the nation's biggest remaining users of the word "Negro," to which its computers have become stubbornly accustomed.) One can hardly look at any Bureau publication without being reminded that in just about every measurable respect the white majority of the United States enjoys bulging advantages over the 22,500,000 blacks who constitute our largest, most troubled, and most troubling minority. It was not until the 1930s that American blacks caught up in numbers with their foreign-born white coresidents, but by 1970 they enjoyed a more than two-to-one edge over that segment of the population. And what a large minority group the American blacks had become! There were more of them than the total population of Canada.

It is no surprise, of course, to perceive that whites

[219]

have it better than blacks, but what was somewhat surprising was the revelation in the 1970 Census that a few of the gaps between American whites and American blacks were finally beginning to narrow. In one area after another, the status of blacks was better, or less bad, vis-à-vis both that of whites and of blacks a decade or more earlier. Still, how one looked at this state of affairs probably depended on who one was. It may have elated white liberals to learn that, although black women still had a higher fertility rate than whites, their production of children had been more sharply curtailed. In 1960, among women fifteen to forty-four, the annual rate of live births per 1,000 women was 162 for blacks and 114 for whites. A decade afterward, the white rate fell to 82, but the black rate fell even faster, to 115—reaching the point where whites had been ten years previous. In 1971, when 26 percent of white mothers between eighteen and twenty-four were declaring that, however many children they already had, they wished to have no more, *36* percent of comparable black mothers were of similar mind. Black mothers of all ages who had five children or more, though, still outnumbered black mothers who had none.

Census figures, incidentally, furnish scant justification for the often repeated charge that most of the children born to black women in poverty are casually conceived illegitimates. In a relative manner of speaking, the contrary is true. What with a general relaxation of morals in the 1960s there was a rise in illegitimate births, but while the rate for white women went up by 53 percent, that for blacks went up by only 17 percent. If one switched from relatives to absolutes, one found that black women had more illegitimate children than white; but, switching back to relatives, one also found that, while in 1961 the blacks were having them at ten times the rate of the whites, by 1970 it was only six to seven times. In any event, for a black woman an illegitimate child was far more likely to become a lifelong family member. Two thirds of all white illegitimate children were put up for adoption; only 7 percent of the black ones. Conversely, whereas only 7 percent of illegitimate white babies remained with their mothers, 90 percent of the black ones did.

Blacks reflecting on statistics might attach less importance to the fact that in the area of birth curtailments they lagged only half a generation or so behind whites than to the fact that a black man who turned twenty-five in 1970 could expect to die six years ahead of his white counterpart—no different at all from the actuarial fate that was ordained for a black man reaching that age in 1960. So, in that vital respect, in ten years the black hadn't gained on the white by so much as a month.

The most consequential gap of all between the races, probably, is the gap in income. If there is ever to be any kind of genuine racial balance in this country, money would seem to be the most promising leveler: Americans have long demonstrated a capacity for loving their neighbors if they are in the same tax bracket. In the last ten years, the average black family has doubled its purchasing power. One third of all black urban families in 1970 had total earnings of $10,000 or more; less than one tenth did in 1960. At the same time, one half of all white families had reached the $10,000 class. So, as many of the once-poor approached the edge of the affluent society, they found themselves still in pursuit of fellow citizens who had moved on into an opulent society. In 1960, the median income for all black families was 55 percent of the white-family median. By 1970, the blacks seemed to have closed that relative gap a bit; they had 61 percent of what the whites had. That seemed to be as close as they could get; in 1971, the figure was back at 60 percent, and in 1972 it was at 59 percent.

And in any event, this gain had been illusory; in absolute terms, the blacks had fallen even further back, by $1,118 a family. For, while their median income had risen from $3,233 to $6,516, at the same time the white median had risen from $5,835 to $10,236. (In 1971, the blacks moved on up to $6,714, and the whites to $10,672. No relative change.) And the annual earnings of the average black with a high-school diploma were still $826 behind those of the average white who'd merely got through eighth grade; the median black *college* graduate, for his part, was $160 behind the median white *high-school* graduate. Similarly, it sounded promising that between 1960 and 1970 there was a 112.6 percent increase in the median income of nonwhite families in the South, while the *white* Southern median scored only a 74.1

percent gain. But 67.8 percent of all black families there, the percentages notwithstanding, remained below the $7,000-a-year level, where they were joined by only 37.3 percent of the whites.

The more that apparent economic advances for blacks are scrutinized, the more it sometimes seems that for them the wheel of fortune is merely a treadmill. There is one kind of black family, for example, that at first glance is statistically indistinguishable from the white: the urban, non-Southern, black household headed by a man under thirty-five. Its median income now matches its white counterpart's, and in those instances where the black man's wife also works, as she is more likely to do than a white wife, the black family's income is actually a bit higher. (Similarly, while all black families in 1971 averaged 1.7 children under eighteen and all white families 1.23, in those families whose head was a professional or technical man, there was just about the same average number for the two races—1.52 for whites, 1.48 for blacks.)

Blacks can hardly be expected to get excited about a kind of equality that involves a black family's almost doubling a white family's efforts to match its rewards. Nor can it be entirely satisfying to know that in recent years the rate of home ownership—presumably a keystone in the arch of the American ideal—has grown faster for blacks than for whites. In 1940, only 23 percent of all the places where blacks lived were owned by their occupants; by 1970, 42 percent of them were. Sounds good at first. But among the quarters that blacks occupied, owned, and rented, were both a disproportionately small share of the newer and presumably better ones, the ones constructed since 1960; and a disproportionately large share of those built before 1939.

The kind of housing that people enjoy is certainly one measure of their relative contentment. According to their numbers, blacks should be saddled with no more than about one tenth of those residential units that either have no bathroom of their own or have to share one with neighbors. In fact, blacks occupied one fifth of these in 1970. By the same token, of all the housing units (405,106 of them) in the country where wood was the principal cooking fuel—which can hardly rate high for congeniality—blacks occupied nearly one half. Poor, largely black Mississippi had 21,191 of these rather special abodes; rich, largely white Connecticut only 915.

One could understand why rural Southern blacks were moving to the cities when one perceived that over half of those who stayed behind lacked decent bathing facilities; for all the squalor of the metropolitan ghettos, only 5 percent of the black-occupied residences there were thus handicapped. But this was no cause for jubilation. True, across the nation, one in every six black residences had bad plumbing, as opposed to two in every five ten years earlier. But, while blacks occupied less than 10 percent of all housing units, they were living in 28 percent of those inadequately equipped.

And when one examined the availability of some

amenities more or less commonplace in American homes today, more striking disparities emerged. Only 2.4 percent of all our housing units were without piped water. Of those with black occupants, 7.9 percent lacked this convenience. The pattern was persistent and pervasive: No flush toilet—3.9 percent of all American residences, 10.4 percent of all black Americans'; no bathtub or shower—4.5 percent for everybody, 12.4 percent for blacks; no complete kitchen facilities—4.2 for everybody, 10.8 percent for blacks; no telephone—12.4 percent for everybody, 30.1 percent for blacks. Only 1.4 percent of all Americans lived in walk-ups four or more stories high, but 3.5 percent of all black Americans had a lot of stairs up which they must lug their groceries.

It is part of the American mythology that it is the nature of the black man to loaf and let his wife support their children. Census statistics do not support this belief. True, young black wives earned on the whole 30 percent more than young white wives in 1970, and more of the former worked—68 percent as opposed to 56 percent; necessity may be the mother of their industriousness. Nonetheless, only one quarter of all black family income was produced by working wives. And because black families tended to run slightly larger than white ones, their available funds per capita were less. Thus, while in metropolitan areas the 1970 median family income for all blacks was 65 percent that of all whites, the income per family *member* was only 55 percent as much.

[225]

Notwithstanding, if family stability is equated with
the presence of an adult male on the scene, black
families were shakier than white. But this situation,
again, is not as deplorable as it is sometimes held to
be. Seventy percent of all black families had a male
head in residence—87 percent of those families with
incomes over $8,000, and 94 percent of those over
$15,000.

The gap between black and white families *is*
widening when it comes to those headed by a woman
alone; the basic structure of American home life may
be less affected by the emancipation of women than
by plain black poverty. Over the last twenty years,
the percentage of white families in this husbandless
category has scarcely changed; it has held steady at 9
percent of the total. Among blacks, it was 17 percent
in 1950, 22 percent in 1960, 29 percent in 1970, and
32 percent in 1972—a rise that must have had all
sorts of painful human consequences. Between 1960
and 1970, while 91 percent of all white children under
eighteen lived with both their parents, the percentage
for black children dropped from 75 percent to 67.
Even in white poverty families, presumably the most
stressful, 44 percent of the children had both parents
in their homes; 24 percent of the black poverty
children did.

What comparatively high-earning black families
there were, in any event, constituted only one tenth
of all the non-Southern black families extant. One
sobering aspect of the surge to the suburbs was that it
had done nothing to bring whites and blacks closer to

economic equilibrium. Just the opposite had occurred. Between 1960 and 1970, there was an *increase* in disparity of income between the largely black residents of the central cities and the no less largely white residents of the suburbs. For median families, the difference between suburban and central-city income was $930 at the beginning of the decade, and $1,850 at the end of it.

Wherever they lived, the blacks had a long way to go to catch up. Even those comparatively few of them who had made it to Stamford, Connecticut, which on a per capita basis is one of the richest cities of the nation, were trailing the pack. More than half of all the 34,700 owner-occupied homes of Stamford were worth over $50,000. But for the 3,893 *black*-owned homes there, the median value was only $30,500, and only twenty-seven of these were in the $50,000-or-over class.

In the tumultuous decade, the black suburban population was increasing, too, and at a slightly higher rate than the white—up by 42 percent nation-wide. But this was not as impressive as it might at first appear to be; there were relatively few suburban blacks at the *start* of the period. The suburban blacks of the District of Columbia actually doubled during the sixties, but this gained them little headway vis-à-vis white suburbanites, for, although the latter scored only a modest percentage increase, their actual numerical increase was larger than the blacks'.

Across the nation, there may be appreciably more blacks in the suburbs than there ever were before, but

at the same time the total black segment of the
American suburban population rose in the sixties
merely from 2.5 percent to 4.2 percent. Whereas,
furthermore, across the country 58 percent of metropolitan whites were living outside the central cities,
only 16 percent of metropolitan blacks were. So the
suburban trend had little effect, all in all, on the lives
of that part of the population that perhaps stood in
greatest need of an upheaval, or simply a patch of
greenery, and this alteration in our national living
habits may actually have put blacks even further
behind whites than they were a generation before.
For the power of our country now resides—literally
—in the suburbs. And while blacks constitute 11
percent of our national population, they constitute
less than half that much of our potent suburban
population.

If young white people seem to think there is little
future in tilling the nation's fields, young black
people have shown no disposition whatever to take
up the slack. Indeed, they are even more swiftly
leaving the farms, where for so long so many of them
toiled. In 1940, one third of all employed blacks of
both sexes worked on farms. As recently as 1960,
slightly more than 12 percent of them did; in 1970, it
was fewer than 4 percent. In the sixties, the nonwhite
farm population dipped from 2,557,000 to 938,000,
and in the second half of that decade, individual
black farm operators fell off from 199,952 to 87,393.
(It is perhaps worth noting that when rural black
women, who traditionally have had an exceedingly

high fertility rate, move to the cities, they quickly begin to reproduce at a much lower rate—at, indeed, almost exactly the same rate as that of native urban blacks.) Those blacks who left the farms were not giving up much. If it was bad that two fifths of all American blacks younger than eighteen lived below the poverty level, it was certainly worse that three quarters of all their peers on farms were under it. Any black these days who exchanged the slums for the soil would, according to the statistics, be trading a frying pan for a fire.

Whatever blacks do to try to learn a living, they seem in general to end up doing it on a meaner and less rewarding scale. It looks good at first to learn that in the United States there were no less than 163,073 businesses owned by blacks in 1970, with total receipts of $4,500,000,000. But most of these were one-person or husband-and-wife businesses. Altogether they had only 151,996 employees—less than one per establishment, and all these employees were concentrated in 38,304 of the businesses. Among the 124,769 companies that had no paid help, the average annual income was $7,000, and probably far more than forty hours a week of labor were expended to earn this pittance. A shoeshine man at a good location can probably take in as much.

Those larger black companies, furthermore, that operated in the areas of building construction, manufacturing, transportation, public utilities, wholesale and retail trade, finance, insurance, and real estate, accounted altogether for less than 1 percent of the total receipts in their specialties. It was no surprise, then, considering that blacks in business had such slim pickings, that though the blacks were 11 percent of the national population, they had only a 5 percent share of the national income.

But in the economic sphere, too, there were indications that blacks were gradually closing the gap between themselves and whites. The percentage of black families with annual incomes under $3,000— about 20 percent—was just the same as the percentage of the white families that had been in the same fix twenty years earlier. Here, again, the blacks were almost exactly a generation behind.

In one other economic respect, a strange equality had been perceived between the races. Andrew F. Brimmer, the first black Governor of the Federal Reserve Board, has pointed out that 86 percent of the total income of whites and 84 percent of the total income of blacks—whatever their dimensions—is derived from earnings. But then comes the crucial difference: The remainder of whites' incomes comes mostly from dividends, interest, royalties, rents, and other unearned increments; the remainder of blacks' incomes comes mostly from welfare and other public assistance. Nearly 5 million black families were on welfare in 1971.

It may be encouraging that, even though blacks' unemployment rates continue, in good times and bad, to be very close to twice those of whites, the kind of work that blacks get when they can get it is gradually being upgraded. In 1960, only 16 percent of all employed nonwhites held white-collar jobs. In 1970, 28 percent did, and this gain represented a substantial increase in jobholders—1 million to 2,400,000. During the decade, the rate of increase of black professional and technical workers (up from 4.7 percent to 9.1 percent of the black labor force) almost precisely matched the rate of decrease of black household workers (down from 15 percent to 7.7 percent). Twice as many professionals and technicals; half as many servants—whether or not we actually see these people, we are told that they are there, so the quality of somebody's life has got to be improving.

Moreover, there have been some quantitative advances. While during the sixties the income of married white blue-collar workers increased by 25 percent, that of married black blue-collar workers went up by 42 percent. And at the same time that these blacks were slowly gaining on the whites, so were all blue-collar workers gaining on all white-collars.

Despite the persistence of discrepancies between their incomes and white incomes, blacks were as aware as anyone else that in general the better educated a person was the better chance he has of getting a decent job. That would have been reason enough to justify the great black migration to metropolitan centers: 25 percent of the blacks who moved from rural to urban communities finished high school, but only 16 percent of those who remained rural throughout their school-age years. Those blacks who were born in the metropolitan areas had a still bigger edge on their country cousins; 40 percent of them went through high school.

Here, once more, all whites had an edge on all blacks. In educational advancement, there was a gap literally the span of a generation between them. The median school years completed by whites in the fifty-five to sixty-four age bracket, for instance, was 11.2 years. That was precisely the median for blacks in the thirty-five to forty-four bracket; they arrived at that point twenty years later. Among younger people, there was far less of a gap: Blacks of twenty and twenty-one had in 1970 a median education of 12.4 years—within easy striking distance of the comparable white median of 12.8. At the other end of the chronological spectrum, there was not a gap but a gulf: Blacks seventy-five years old and over had a median education of 4.6 years, and whites of the same age 8.6 years.

By the time the educational gap is fully closed, which could be soon, a sizable bloc of Americans will be affected by this evolutionary step toward equality: In 1970, although blacks came to only 11 percent of the population, 15 percent of all children under five were black, and these preschoolers amounted to 12 percent of the entire black American population. By the time they reach seventy-five, they could be the best-educated septuagenarians the nonwhite world has ever known.

Much of the foregoing has been quantitative, but the gaps in quality of American education are diminishing, too. In 1964, slightly more than half of all black college students were attending institutions that were predominantly black. In 1970, three quarters of these black students were in predominantly white institutions—where, as things worked out, a good many of them devoted themselves energetically to proclaiming their blackness and separateness and looking askance at all integrationist overtures.

Over that six-year stretch, the total number of blacks in college had jumped from 234,000 to 530,000, and there were more men in the group than women. This represented a significant change in the pattern of black life. It had long been the case that most of the jobs open to black women were in domestic service or in teaching—these latter mainly in segregated schools. To get teaching certificates, they needed academic credentials, and for that reason there had always been a substantially greater number of black women attending college than black men. Now, the brothers are catching up with their sisters.

At the same time, younger black men had been dropping out of school at a far higher rate than comparable whites. (Forty-four percent of black men who were between thirty and thirty-four in 1970 had never finished high school; it was 25 percent for the whites.) Another narrowing gap was discernible here. Between 1969 and 1970, the proportion of metropolitan white males who'd got through secondary school rose only from 62.2 percent to 63.2 percent. The black increase was a bit swifter—from 42.1 percent to

44.8 percent. Over the decade that ended in 1970, the increase was more noticeable: Whereas in 1960, only 38 percent of blacks of both sexes between twenty-five and twenty-nine had finished high school, ten years later 56 percent had.

During the 1970s, it is estimated that 2,800,000 blacks under thirty-five who have a high-school education will join the country's labor pool. At the start of the decade, their prospects of getting jobs were not particularly good. For all whites, the unemployment rate stood at just over 4 percent, and for all blacks at just over 8 percent. Gloomy as that sounded, it could be optimistically interpreted: For 1970 was the first year in a generation during which the overall black unemployment rate was less than double the white rate. The 1971 average rates were 9.9 percent for blacks and 5.4 percent for whites. By 1972, the frustrating old two-to-one ratio had returned.

Moreover, there were significant qualitative gains in black employment. During the 1960s, the number of craftsmen and operatives in the white labor force, those men and women emancipated from unskilled work, rose by a mere 7 percent, while the blacks in that classification rose by 46 percent. And, while in 1960 only 16.1 percent of employed nonwhites had white-collar jobs, by 1970, 27.9 percent of them did. In a still higher category—professional, technical, and kindred workers—whites increased by 45 percent, and blacks simultaneously by 131 percent. Among clerical workers, it was a 36 percent gain for the whites, and 121 percent for the blacks. And of the 259,272 computer specialists calculated by the Bureau's computers to have been in the labor force in 1970, a not unpresentable 9,034 were black; of the 50,254 women, 2,720 were black.

It is worth bearing in mind, though, that while some of the black percentages rose impressively, there had been only a small base to build on. (For computer specialists, of course, there was *no* base, since they hadn't been singled out in 1960.) For all the headway blacks have made, there was still the hard fact to face that while 41 percent of all male white workers over sixteen enjoyed white-collar status, only 20 percent of the black males did. More than half of all black women—their few computer specialists notwithstanding—were still working at jobs that could only be described as menial.

And, although by 1970 there were far more blacks than ever before in the higher-rated employment areas, even so only 7 percent of the nation's professional, technical, and kindred workers were black (among them, 2 percent of the doctors), only 5 percent of its foremen, only 4 percent of its managers, officials, and proprietors. In the nine American industries with comparatively high hourly wage levels—printing and publishing, chemicals, primary metals, fabricated metals, nonelectrical machinery, electrical machinery, transportation equipment, air transportation, and instruments—blacks held 8 percent of the jobs, which was not too far from their proportion to the total population. But within these industries, they had only 1 percent of the best jobs, and 17 percent of the worst ones. In air transportation, there were only 17,000 blacks among 327,000 employees—half of them in the least remunerative spots, and practically none of them in the most.

In those industries that employed blacks in larger numbers—among them, tobacco, health, transit, hotels, eating places, and repair services—there were never more than 8 percent of them in the higher-paid jobs, and in only one instance (local transit) were fewer than 25 percent of them in the lower regions. And, while blacks held 15 percent of all federal jobs, they had only 3 percent of the decision-making ones, and less than 10 percent of all those that paid $8,000 a year or more.

So it went. It didn't really go very far. Besides, although there were demonstrable and perhaps even dramatic advances among blacks in education, income, and status between 1960 and 1970, this progress had resulted in no discernible letup in their expressions of dissatisfaction. The principal reason probably had nothing to do with statistics; more likely, it was a case of their expectations, however momentarily satisfied, simply continuing to rise. Just about everybody, after all, wants to be better off than he is; and he is not apt to be overly impressed by the news that he is somewhat better off than he used to be ten years earlier.

XIV

✩ ✩ ✩ ✩ ✩ ✩

The Opulent Society

W<small>HEN</small> J<small>OHN</small> K<small>ENNETH</small> G<small>ALBRAITH</small> <small>WROTE</small> *The Affluent Society* in 1958, there was an electric coffee pot in one of every two American homes. By 1970, 86 percent of all families had one of them (and this even though some families that could doubtless afford them shunned them or drank tea). In many small respects, the once affluent society had become what, by 1958 criteria, was an opulent one, or at the very least an electric one. Between 1961 and 1970, 47 million electric hair dryers were sold in the United States, and in just the six years after 1964, 22 million electric carving knives—one of these, unless some people were hoarding them, for nearly every three households. During the 1960s, while the population was going up by 13 percent, the consumption of electrical energy went up by 100 percent.

When it came to that, between 1930 and 1960 the population had risen by 63 percent, and the consumption of crude petroleum and natural gas by, respectively, 300 percent and 900 percent. The per capita oil consumption of the United States is three times that of Japan. To produce the amount of energy consumed throughout the world today requires the equivalent of 1.9 metric tons of coal per capita. The per capita figure for Ghana is .16 ton, for West Germany, 5.1 tons, for Canada, 9.1 tons, and for the unchallengeably energetic United States, 11.1 tons.

The average number of radios per American family was three in 1960; a decade later, it was five. Radios are small, and often portable, and in most instances not too costly. What is perhaps more illustrative of the recent change in American living and spending habits was that, whereas in 1960 only 12.4 percent of all families had an air-conditioner, ten years afterward the percentage had tripled. In New York City, even 10 percent of those families with incomes under $3,000—families, that was, far below the poverty level—had their own air-conditioners.

What Americans choose to spend their money on, and how much they pay for this or that commodity, has long been of interest to their government. The Consumer Price Index, drawn up for many years by the Bureau of Labor Statistics, is the basis of that Bureau's periodically revised Cost of Living Index, which has a direct impact on the incomes of, among others, some 4 million workers covered by union contracts with escalation clauses, and millions of others who receive pensions and Social Security or Veterans Administration benefits. The nation's poverty level is also computed from the Cost of Living Index. It was no particular problem for the Department of Labor to keep abreast of current prices, but, because it was its practice to survey Americans' buying habits only once every ten years, there was some doubt about what items it should concentrate on. Habits change; it does not reveal much to inquire into the purchases of coal stoves, because they are not much in use anymore.

Family budgets can be radically redrawn in a decade. Between 1950 and 1960, for instance, the amount of money allocated by all American households for food and beverages went down from 31.4 to 26 percent, the amount for housing up from 27.2 to 29.5 percent, for clothing down from 11.5 to 10.4 percent, for automobile expenses up from 11.6 to 13 percent, for medical care up from 5.2 to 6.6 percent, for everything else up from 13.1 to 14.5 percent. In 1970, of the $615,800,000,000 spent by all Americans on personal consumption, 23.3 percent of it went for food, beverages, and tobacco, 14.8 percent for housing, 13.9 percent for household operations, 12.6 percent for transportation, 10.1 percent for clothing, accessories, and jewelry, 7.7 percent for medical bills, 6.3 percent for recreation, 5.8 percent for personal business matters, 1.6 percent for personal care, and 3.9 percent for all other outlays.

This, then, was the basic structure of the American 1970 budget. A family hewing strictly to it, and having the national median income of $10,000, would have spent $2,330 on food, beverages, and tobacco, $1,480 on housing, $1,390 on running its household, $1,260 on transportation, $1,010 on clothing, accessories, and jewelry (costume jewelry, one would surmise), $770 on medical costs, $630 on recreation, $580 on personal business, $160 on personal care, and $390 on everything else.

At the start of 1972, the government, aware though it was that in the previous years the price of frozen orange juice had gone up by 36 percent and that of nylon hose down by 3 percent, decided that it wanted to learn more about Americans' purchasing quirks. So the Census Bureau undertook a Survey of Consumer Expenditures among 17,000 carefully selected families, who were informed that they would be "helping to create an up-to-date market basket."

At that, it was to be only relatively up-to-date; the survey was scheduled to end in March 1974, but the results of it were not to be made public until some time in 1975 or 1976. The market basket was an extraordinarily capacious one; those helping to create it were being asked to furnish information about their purchases of, among other consumer goods, sweaters, fur jackets and stoles, women's pantsuits, dungarees and jeans, culottes, jumpers, blouses, girdles, body stockings, pantyhose, tights, housecoats, and brunch coats. A nation that cares about brunch coats is a nation that *cares*.

Concurrently, 19,000 additional households in seventy-eight Standard Metropolitan Statistical Areas and 100 other places, both rural and urban, were being asked to keep a daily diary over a two-week stretch, and to itemize every single thing they bought. When this program was launched, there was some doubt as to whether Americans would go to the trouble of getting involved in it. The idea had been tried successfully in England, but there the participants had been paid for their pains. The Census Bureau decided that to try anything like that would be politically risky; someone would be sure to accuse it of indulging in federal handouts.

So the diary program has been strictly voluntary, and the individuals invited to take part in it, egged on by Census Bureau operatives working out of some two dozen field offices, have on the whole been gratifyingly cooperative. *Their* market basket is cornucopian. They have been asked to recall and recount whether each purchase of milk they make is whole, skimmed, or half-and-half; to distinguish among different kinds of bread and flour; to tell whether their vegetables are fresh, frozen, canned, or packaged; and to jot down every expenditure for light bulbs, nails, postage stamps, diapers, and random cups of coffee extracted from vending machines.

The dividing line between what used to be thought of as necessities and of luxuries has, for an enormous number of Americans, become blurred. In 1970, we were a nation in which 99 percent of its 63 million households had a refrigerator, a gas or electric range, and an electric iron; in which more households—29.3 percent of the total—had two cars than had none; and in which as many had television sets as had toilets. There were no more than half a million homes that didn't have both. In 19 percent of our households there was a dishwasher, in 41 percent a clothes dryer, and in 91 percent a vacuum cleaner.

However messily we might treat our outdoor environment—we were releasing 208 million tons of manmade wastes into the air annually, 51 percent of it from transportation sources—indoors we had achieved an unparalleled capacity for tidiness. And, however unliberated some of our women might feel politically, socially, and economically, domestically they had been freed from manual drudgery to a degree beyond their mothers' dreams.

Residents of other countries, where median income figures are apt to fluctuate between decades by tens of dollars rather than by thousands, must occasionally think that some of our statistics are misprints. Even 41 percent of all Americans living in poverty had a car. Of those with incomes over $15,000 in 1970, which hardly qualified them by their country's standards as rich, 96 percent had one car and 63 percent at least two. By July of 1971, the Census Bureau reckoned that some 20 million households—nearly one third of the national total—owned at least two cars.

Americans spent $80,000,000,000—eighty billion dollars—that year on such household durables as furniture, carpets, radios, television sets, phonographs, kitchen equipment, air-conditioners, and so forth. That sounds like a lot, but it was less than half of the $180 billion they disbursed to buy automobiles: $120 billion worth of new ones and $60 billion of used. Here again one found the familiar quantitative gap between the races. Whites averaged sixteen new and twenty-four used cars per hundred families; blacks, four new ones and sixteen used ones per hundred. In all their automobiles, Americans clicked off 312 billion miles—1,500 per person. But most of them didn't get very far; two thirds of the nation never travels, by any means, more than 100 miles from home. A mid-1972 survey of those who did break this barrier revealed that during the first five months of that year 61,288,000 Americans went on trips of over 100 miles and covered 125,280,000,000 person–miles, 80,015,000,000 of these by motor vehicle, 41,194,000,000 by air, and only 819,000,000 by train. More than half of all these person–miles were accounted for by suburbanites, who had the most cars and the most money.

Nearly 90 percent of all the trips that Americans took were in automobiles (they also had 5 million trucks that were used mainly for personal transport), and of the $11 billion that, not including purchases of vehicles, they spent on transportation annually, $8,500,000,000 went toward the upkeep of their automobiles. The total that individual Americans lavished on driving—on cars, parts, gas, and oil, but omitting highways—came to considerably more than what was spent on all education, public and private, at all levels, from all sources. The prevalence of automobiles has even markedly affected our vital statistics. In 1968, for instance, the median age of all Americans dying from heart disease was seventy-five;

from cancer, sixty-seven; and from accidents, forty-one.

It followed logically enough that in 1970 there were 912,410 automobile mechanics in the country—more of them than carpenters, nearly twice as many of them as doctors, dentists, and other practitioners put together. (California had the most mechanics: 87,272. Oklahoma had an almost identical number of mechanics and health workers—12,941 of the former, 12,945 of the latter.) There were 2,138,880 additional workers engaged in the manufacture of motor vehicles and other means of transport—more than there were in the processing of food; and still another 1,698,694 people devoted themselves to retailing vehicles and operating service stations—more than the total employed by utilities and sanitary services.

The $20 billion that all our governmental agencies spent on highways in 1970 was more than they laid out for police, fire, and sanitation services, more than was allotted to hospitals, about the same as their welfare costs. It is sometimes charged by people opposed to welfare programs that one of their drawbacks is that they benefit only a fraction of the population; those who were on welfare and didn't have automobiles (57.5 percent of the households with incomes under $3,000 had none) might logically have complained about all those funds poured into highways.

Only 17.5 percent of all households (43.1 percent of black households) had no car available in 1970, and 5.5 percent of all households had three or more cars.

Eighty percent of all the *people* in the country had access to at least one car, and nearly 30 percent to two or more. (In the West, it was 40 percent.) Among households in the $15,000-or-higher income bracket, 96.6 percent had at least one car; perhaps more remarkably, 8.3 percent of the households *under* $5,000 had two or more. These under-$5,000 households (32.5 percent of the lot) owned 18.3 percent of all cars. Blacks may be concentrated in the cities, where presumably there is less need for cars than elsewhere; no matter, 52.5 percent of *all* black households had a car. It was understandable that cars should figure importantly in suburban living: 39.5 percent of all suburban families had two or more, and 15 percent of all those suburban families consisting of a husband and wife and at least one child over fifteen had three or more.

Of the nation's 76,852,389 workers in 1970, all of whom had to get to work by one means or another, 59,722,550 used automobiles. Only about 9 million of them rode in somebody else's vehicle; that means that every weekday there were more than 50 million one-person cars on the road. (How much richer and environmentally purer the quality of our life could be if only some respected national personage like Billy Graham or Oral Roberts would popularize the slogan, "Drive thy neighbor!") In California, 83.5 percent of all workers went to work by car. Even in the nation's central cities, where 25,050,898 workers lived, 17,313,779 used autos, and a mere 1,974,273 walked. Fifty million Americans—the same number who ride to work alone—claimed they also walked for pleasure.

Between 1960 and 1970, despite the adjurations of doctors and mayors, the number of Americans who walked to *work* dropped from 6,400,000 to 5,700,000—a decline probably less reflective of apprehensions about urban mugging than of the lapse of farm employment. (In big agricultural states like the Dakotas, 15 percent of all employed persons still walked to work, many of them merely by stepping out of their front doors.) It may astonish some people to learn that in Los Angeles, despite all the freeways, 5.4 percent of the workers walked; in Boston, 11 percent did. Alaska led all the states in the proportion of those workers who used neither autos nor public transport nor their feet; presumably airplanes, bicycles, boats, and dogsleds were involved.

Whatever the reason for it—maybe the known success of the highway lobbyists in Washington—only 8.9 percent of all the workers used any kind of public transportation in 1970. As the reliance on cars increased in the sixties from 64 to 77 percent, so did the use of mass transport diminish from 12.1 to 8.5 percent. Nationwide, less than 10 percent of all workers—only 6,514,012 of them—went to work by bus, streetcar, subway, elevated train, or railroad. Of all 58,227,931 *urban* workers, only a little over 10 percent depended on public transport—a trifling 4,115,978 on streetcars, an even more minuscule 1,761,723 on subways or els, and a laughable 472,553 on railroads. (In the entire South, nobody went to work by train.) Outside the Northeast, only 2,967,476 people in the entire country used public transport; it is easy to see why Congressmen from other regions need pay little heed to demands for urban rapid transit.

Even in New York City, sometimes known as Baghdad-on-the-Subway, only about half the workers took to the underground. If many of the 3,000,000 working men and women in New York didn't use subways or els, there would have been precious few people who did at all; for the New Yorkers who depended on rapid transit added up to 80 percent of the Americans who did. Washington, D.C., would seem at first glance to have set an estimable example for the rest of the country: Only 49.1 percent of *its* workers used automobiles, and it thus was the sole place of consequence where fewer than half of the resident labor force rode on its own wheels. But on closer scrutiny the District of Columbia turned out to be not much different from any other metropolis: Many of its jobs were filled by Marylanders and Virginians, and 79.7 percent of the former and 79.9 percent of the latter traveled to work by car—just *over* the national average of 77.7 percent.

There was no skyrocketing surge of purchasing power to account for all the buying that characterized the 1960s—merely heightened appetites. Between 1960 and 1970, median income went up by 43 percent, but at the same time consumer prices went up by 31.1 percent. Consumer credit stood, breathtakingly, at $127 billion. In his book *Rich Man, Poor Man,* Herman P. Miller, for many years the knowledgeable chief of the Population Division of the Census Bureau, noted that in 1960, in the poorest county of the poorest state of the Union—Tunica County, in northwest Mississippi—37 percent of all households had a washing machine, 46 percent a car, and 52 percent a television set. Tunica County has not lost its unhappy distinction, but its inhabitants have duly shared in the national acquisitiveness: In 1970, 61 percent of its households had a washing machine, 61 percent a car, and 86 percent a television set.

Tunica County is nearly three quarters black, and in 1970 Mississippi had the highest proportion of poor blacks—67.1 percent of its black residents being below the poverty level—of any state. Mississippi also had the highest incidence of poverty regardless of race: 28.9 percent of all its families. At the other end of the economic spectrum stood Connecticut, with only 5.3 percent of all its families and 19.2 percent of its black families suffering from statistical deprivation. In the fall of 1972, the magazine *Lifestyle* described Connecticut (with a $3,900 per capita income) and Mississippi ($1,597 per capita) as the best and worst states in the nation.

The evidence was persuasive. Connecticut's median family income of $11,811 was the highest for 1970 of any state save Alaska, and Alaska didn't really count because of its comparatively astronomical cost of living. Mississippi, with a $6,071 median, was the lowest. While 31.1 percent of all Connecticut families had broken the $15,000 income barrier, only 8.3 percent of Mississippi's had. Mississippi was the only state in which as many as 10 percent of all families had incomes under $2,000; and 6.6 percent of its families were under $1,000. Mississippi led all the states in the percentage of its families—11.1—receiving public assistance; conversely, Connecticut led in very high incomes, with 1.5 percent of all its families over the $50,000 mark.

In Connecticut, 67.9 percent of all eighteen- to twenty-four-year-olds had finished high school; in Mississippi, 46.9 percent. In Connecticut, 7.8 percent of this age group had finished college; in Mississippi, 2.9 percent. The median value of a Connecticut house was $25,500, and of a Mississippi house $11,200. Among all Mississippi households, black and white together, 24.3 percent lacked some or all plumbing, 18.8 percent lacked a complete kitchen, and 18.7 percent were without a flush toilet; for Connecticut, the comparable percentages were 2.17, 2.4, and 0.3. For blacks in the two states, things were even worse: 43.6 percent of Mississippi's had inadequate kitchens and 41.5 percent no toilet; Connecticut's comparable percentages were 1.7 and 0.2.

As Mississippi's Tunica was the nation's most pitiable county, so was Connecticut's Fairfield County perhaps its most enviable, and not merely because Tunica is landlocked and Fairfield borders on the Long Island Sound. Fairfield, with a 1970 population of 792,814 (21.3 percent higher than in

1960), is much bigger than Tunica, with 11,854 (29.5 percent *lower* than in 1960). It is one of the incomprehensibilities of statistical analysis that, despite Fairfield's wealth and growth and Tunica's poverty and regression, between 1965 and 1970, 160 people moved from the environs of the former to the latter, and absolutely not a soul in the opposite direction. The contrasts between these two polar counties are singular, and it is at about this point in a narrative of this sort that the author pauses and asks himself: How can one possibly put together a book about the Census and not include a single chart or graph?

Very well, then.

	FAIRFIELD	TUNICA
Area	626 sq. mi.	458 sq. mi.
Density of population	1,266.5 per sq. mi.	25.9 per sq. mi.
Black percentage of population	7.6	72.8
Births per thousand women	331	688
No. of persons per household	3.19	3.83
Residents of Chinese origin	773	4
Residents of Japanese origin	413	1*
Residents of East Indian origin	346	1*
Median age	30.7	19.9
Males	29.3	18.8
Females	32	21.9
White males	30.1	29.8
White females	33	33.5
Black males	21.1	16.8
Black females	23.6	18.7

* The Indian is a male, and the Japanese a female. Are they a couple, and what in the world are they doing there?

	FAIRFIELD	TUNICA
Median age, 1960	32.9	18.8
Percentage of divorced men	1.44	0.76
Percentage of divorced women	2.44	0.95
Percentage of widows	8.9	11.5
Percentage of whites sixty-five or over	9.8	11.4
Percentage of blacks sixty-five or over	4.2	11.9
Percentage of rural farm population	1.0	51.6
Percentage foreign-born	9.8	0.1
Percentage native of foreign or mixed parentage	23.9	0.7
Percentage of children in elementary private schools	18.9	9.2
Percentage of fourteen- to seventeen-year-olds in school	95.8	81.1
Median school years completed, for population twenty-five and over	12.3	7.1
Percentage of persons under eighteen living with both parents	87.6	64.5
Cumulative fertility rate, women thirty-five to forty-four	2,654	5,334
Percentage of males eighteen to twenty-four in labor force	71	54.3
Percentage of civilian labor force unemployed	3.3	10.3
Percentage employed in manufacturing	35.1	13

	FAIRFIELD	TUNICA
Percentage in white-collar jobs	56.5	24.9
Percentage working outside county of residence	13.6	4.8
Percentage working fifty to fifty-two weeks in 1969	59.5	38.7
Median family income	$13,086	$2,885
Percentage of families under poverty level	4.6	55.6
Percentage of families with incomes of $15,000 or more	39.8	4.6
Percentage of natives of native parentage	66.4	99.2
Percentage born in state of residence	49.7	92.3
Foreign-stock population	266,647	99
from United Kingdom	22,027	0
" Ireland	16,561	0
" Sweden	5,624	0
" Germany	18,267	0
" Poland	21,002	0
" Czechoslovakia	11,596	0
" Austria	8,817	0
" Hungary	14,019	0
" U.S.S.R.	12,219	0
" Italy	59,633	0
" Canada	19,140	27
" Mexico	259	60
" Cuba	2,418	0
" Other America	7,601	6
Persons of Spanish language	28,346	82

	FAIRFIELD	TUNICA
Puerto Rican birth or parentage	14,167	7
Numbers in college, 1970	6,849	9
Veterans, percentage of males sixteen and over	47	20.3
Served in Vietnam	14,446	67
Percentage, ages twenty and twenty-one, in school	37.1	11.5
Percentage of males twenty-five and over with no years of school	1.2	10.7
Percentage of high-school graduates (male)	59.9	18
Number of children ever born per married woman thirty-five to forty-four	2.85	5.5
Percentage of males sixteen and over in labor force	81.3	56.4
Percentage of males unemployed	3.1	11.9
Percentage of females over sixteen in labor force	44	32.7
Percentage of females unemployed	3.5	7.8
Engineers	8,917	0
Physicians, dentists, and practitioners	2,568	0
Farm laborers and foremen	527	539
Median earnings, males sixteen and over	$9,315	$2,827
Percentage of families with incomes over $25,000	14.2	1.7
Population density per housing unit	3.2	3.9

[255]

	FAIRFIELD	TUNICA
Per capita income	$4,676	$1,145
Mean size of family	3.7	5.57
Percentage of housing units lacking some plumbing	2.2	62.7
Percentage without piped water	0.06	53.5
Percentage without flush toilet	0.16	58.7
Percentage without bathtub or shower	0.63	59.9
Percentage without complete kitchen facilities	1.1	58.5
Median value of owner-occupied housing units	$34,700	$9,700
Percentage of all-year-round structures built 1939 or earlier	40	50
Percentage without telephone	5.4	52.5
Percentage with three or more cars available	8	1
Number of units heated by wood	87	645
Percentage without clothes washer	22	32
Percentage without dryer	50	66
Percentage with two or more television sets	33	14

The comparisons would be even more striking if, in the case of Tunica, its 3,225 whites were culled from the totals and the remaining 8,614 blacks were left to their own devices.

In 1971, the median income for all American families went above $10,000 for the first time in

history; it reached $10,285, and, barring some un-
likely deflationary upheaval in our economy, is
unlikely soon again to revert to four figures. With
more than 50 percent of our families over $10,000—
quadruple the number in 1960—there were also some
519,021 households, plus 100,000 or so scattered
individuals, with annual incomes over $25,000 and a
further 398,000 families over $50,000. While the poor
may be less poor today than they were a generation
ago, however, they have no good reason to believe
that the rich are not just as rich as ever, and maybe
getting richer. Between 1958 and 1970 the lowest one
fifth of American wage-earners' share of the national
earnings dropped from 5.1 to 4.6 percent, while the
portion that went to the highest one fifth of them rose
from 38.2 to 40.6 percent.

Families with incomes over $10,000 were 47.4
percent better off in 1972 than in 1958; those in the
$7,500–$9,999 category 39 percent ahead; those in
the $5,000–$7,499 category 29.6 percent ahead; those
in the $3,000–$4,999 category 24.9 percent ahead; but
those under $3,000 only 18 percent ahead. (Between
1961 and 1971, while the median dollar income for
everybody went up 79 percent, in terms of purchasing
power there was only an actual 33 percent increase.)
The poorest 20 percent of our families, those roughly
10 million of them with incomes under $5,000,
received in all less than 6 percent of the total national
income; the richest 20 percent, those also roughly 10
million families over $14,000, received 40 percent of

it. And the richest 5 percent of the lot owned 14 percent of all the assets we could count.

Such are the statistics on which discontent subsists. In any event, by 1970 there were so many millionaires extant in America—a couple of hundred thousand, most days, depending on the vagaries of the stock market—that the only kind of Mr. Moneybags worth gaping at was the kind with an adjusted gross *income* of $1 million a year. The country harbored 642 of them.

In 1972, the personal income of all Americans came close to the trillion-dollar mark, but the advent of this milestone was hardly a cause for celebration, occurring as it did at a time when, because of inflation, there was actually *less* purchasing power for every American than there'd been a couple of years earlier. Still, one trillion dollars ($1,000,000,000,000) came to about $5,000 a year in income for every one of our roughly 200 million people. To divide our massive spoils in such fashion is, of course, indicative of the occasional ludicrousness of averaging, inasmuch as nearly 10 percent of the sum ended up in the clutches of just 1 percent of the population, which could thus add a hefty share of the national income to its continuing domination of the national principal.

Annual incomes aside, it is amazing how little money most Americans really have. There are probably 5,000 of us with a net worth of $10 million or more—and, contrary to the belief that women hold the pursestrings of the nation, men outnumber them in this select, manipulative group by two to one—but at the same time the median of liquid assets for all American families was, in 1970, a paltry $800. Only one of every eight families had assets of more than $10,000, and one of every six families in this all-but-trillion-dollar-a-year country had no assets whatever. In other lands, it may appear that Uncle Sam wears a diamond-studded vest; to many of his nephews and nieces, it merely seems that they live awfully close to the vest.

The proliferation of nonessentials in American homes has been partly the result, too, of changes in consuming habits. The year 1970 was a significant one because, for the first time in history, Americans spent less than half their income on food, clothing, shelter, and utilities. We had come far fast in self-indulgence, or, at any rate, in making choices about the use of our money. At the start of the twentieth century, few Americans had comparable options. Eighty percent of their expenditures were on basics. Between 1940 and 1970, the amount of American income spent on essential goods—food and clothing, for the most part—dropped from 50 to 39 percent.

Going into the 1970s, the American people, after having also taken care of their housing expenses, had left over, by Census Bureau calculation, something in the neighborhood of $150 billion a year to disburse at their discretion—the not inconsiderable sum of about $750 per capita. Facing bravely up to the challenge of getting rid of all this cash, the Americans, who in

1950 had spent about $3 billion on musical instruments, phonographs and records, radios, television sets, and attendant repairs, managed to allocate $10 billion to them. Some cynics might express surprise that the national bill for T.V. repairs alone did not exceed that sum.

In 1970, Americans lavished more on cosmetics and other beautifiers, and also on tobacco, than on private education and research together. Americans could, and did, spend $40 million on recreation—more than twice what they allotted to religious and welfare activities. About the only thing they spent *less* money on than they had a generation earlier was the movies. In 1950, the country had 19,000 motion-picture theaters, and their box offices took in $1,376,000,000; by 1970, there were five thousand fewer theaters, and their receipts—higher admission prices notwithstanding—had fallen off by $214 million.

When it came to recreation, America's favorite turned out—statistics thus ringingly corroborating folklore—to be the picnic. In 1970, America had 82 million picnickers. Nobody has undertaken to count the ants they attracted. Nearly as many people—77,300,000 of them—went swimming in the course of the year. There was a nice balance between participation in other outdoor games and sports and attendance at them; the 60 million active sportsmen numbered only 600,000 more than the spectator kind.

There were 49,400,000 fishermen, 26,900,000 hunters, and 7,500,000 birdwatchers. Fishing, it was agreeable to note, was both cheaper and more popular (not to mention safer) than hunting. Our 22,184,000 *licensed* hunters spent $101,608,000 in 1970 for their permits; our 31,136,000 licensed anglers were charged only $90,864,000 for theirs. And even without gun controls, whereas fishermen outnumbered hunters by less than 3 million in 1950, in 1970 there were almost 9 million more of the former than of the latter. The Census does not keep us up on taxidermists.

XV

☆　☆　☆　☆　☆　☆

The Poverty People

O N THE BASIS OF THE STIFF, COMPUTERIZED TABLES
churned out by the Census Bureau, the United States
sometimes seems unbendingly compartmentalized
and polarized—a country sharply divided between
rural and urban, east and west, north and south, male
and female, old and young, black and white, rich and
poor. Indeed the poorest of the poor, those who slip
below the official poverty point, sometimes seem to
be inhabiting a private enclave of their own, an
economic ghetto that the world's most prosperous
nation (unless one wishes to quibble about Kuwait or
Nauru) cannot eradicate.

Even the cost of poverty is going up. The line was
drawn in 1970 at $3,968 for a family of four—an
increase of $1,000 over the 1959 cutoff point—but by
1971 it had reached $4,137 and, by the start of 1973,
$4,275. This was for nonfarm families; farm families,
who presumably could live at least in part off the
land, were not considered poor if they had as much
as $3,643. The government makes slight additional

concessions to larger families; the maximum a seven-person nonfarm family could receive and still be poor was $6,983; for the same-sized farm family the maximum was $5,947.

More than 25,600,000 Americans—7,400,000 of them black and 2,400,000 of them of Spanish-speaking origin—lived in 1971 in a state of poverty. Of all the families in the nation, 5.3 percent were receiving some form of public assistance: Of all white families, 4 percent; of Spanish-speaking-origin families, 12.6 percent; of black families, 17.6 percent. The poverty enclave had no geographical bounds. There were almost exactly the same number of poor people outside the big metropolitan centers as within them. Of those communities with a population of 50,000 or more, Brownsville, Texas, had in 1970 the largest proportion of poverty families—40.8 percent of all its families in residence; Arlington Heights, Illinois, could, with 1.4 percent, boast the lowest proportion of the very poor.

Their overall dispersion notwithstanding, many of the poor do actually live in physical ghettos, and, as the government has defined poverty people, so also has it defined "poverty areas." They are those in which, according to several elaborate formulas, are generally to be found the highest concentrations of families that exhibit characteristics associated with inferior standards of living—bad housing, low income, broken households, little education, limited employment skills. In 1960, when the Office of Economic Opportunity was set up to try to cope specifically with the problems of the poor, the Census Bureau determined that there were 193 such poverty areas. By 1970, the formulas had been changed, so there was no precisely comparable figure, but there was no reason to believe that the number had diminished.

In the poverty areas of the nation's central cities, there was a 19 percent increase in population in the 1960s—from 13,348,000 to 15,882,000, or from 33 percent of all central-city people to 39 percent. Thus the least attractive sections of our least viable residential communities were increasingly sheltering more and more of our hapless. And the poverty areas, what was more, were becoming increasingly segregated; the poor could only aspire to the privileges of the rich, but they could readily share their prejudices. Cleveland, for instance, at last count had nine poverty areas. Six of them were 94 percent black and the other three were 94 percent white.

The poor are, properly, so much of a concern to the nation that since 1968 the Census Bureau has had a special department to keep tabs on them. It has not concentrated as intensively on the rich, who have less need of its ministrations. (When a Rockefeller wants to find something out, he can conduct his own survey, and not infrequently does.) In the fall of 1971, though, with an election year coming up, the Nixon administration decided that to keep putting out studies stressing the word "poverty" had a defeatist ring to it, so "low-income" was substituted. At about the same time, the Bureau of Labor Statistics was enjoined to quit putting out bulletins—based on Census Bureau data—about joblessness among black Americans.

When the halt was declared, the unemployment rate in urban poverty areas had just gone up from 10.1 percent to 10.4 percent. The rate for whites in those areas presumably warranted disclosure; it had gone down from 9.1 percent to 8 percent. But it would have been hard to reveal that without concurrently revealing that the *black* rate had gone up from 11.9 percent to 14.1 percent. What was worse, although even in poverty circles blacks were a minority group, their jobless in these poverty areas had for the first time overtaken the white jobless numerically—342,000 to 298,000.

Far worse still was the status of teenagers in poverty areas. While the unemployment rate for whites in that age group and environment had fallen from 23.8 percent to 19 percent, that for blacks had risen from 36.2 percent to 37.1 percent. One would think that the situation could hardly have got graver, but it could: While in all metropolitan areas about one fifth of all black families were below the poverty line, in the rest of the country nearly half of them were.

About the only cheerful aspect of the poverty picture was that overall it was less discouraging than it had been before. In 1959, there were 39,500,000 people living in poverty—22 percent of the entire population. By 1971, the 25,600,000 who remained in that category comprised only 13 percent of all of us.

Poor whites had decreased by 38 percent, poor blacks by 29 percent. (As California had become preeminent among the states in most measurements, so did it harbor most of the poor—just short of 2 million of them; the golden state was not without its baser metal.) One of every ten white Americans lived in a state of poverty, and one out of every three blacks. At the start of the sixties, three quarters of all nonmetropolitan blacks were in poverty; a decade later, only half this group was. But, such gains notwithstanding, blacks were not escaping from poverty as fast as whites. Blacks used to be 27 percent of all the American poor, but by 1970, though they were only 11 percent of the total population, they were 31 percent of the poverty population. Indeed, they were close to becoming a majority of the welfare population. In 1971, whites still constituted 47 percent of those receiving aid to dependent children, but blacks were up to 44 percent.

One third of all poverty families were headed by black women—706,000 such families, compared with 600,000 black poverty families headed by men. For the whites in poverty, the opposite held true: 2,595,000 male-headed families and 1,021,000 female-headed ones. This would seem to suggest that a conventionally structured family is no guarantee against impoverishment. On the other hand, having a male wage-earner around is certainly a help, for, while poverty has generally been diminishing, that has been anything but the case among families headed solely by women. Nationwide, as of March

1972, 9.4 percent of all white families were headed by a woman, 29 percent of Puerto Rican families, and 31.8 percent of black families.

Women presided over 11 percent of all American families, 37 percent of all poverty families, and 57 percent of all black poverty families. In the nation's metropolitan areas, there was in the 1960s an increase of 29 percent among poverty families headed by women, and of 40 percent among those headed by black women. These last unfortunates had an average of 3.5 children apiece to cope with (the average for poverty families headed by white males, by contrast, was 1.8), and of all poverty families with two or more children, 71 percent were nonwhite. And what few resources they could muster had to be distributed in a fashion not common to the general populace. In 1970, the Census Bureau made a special survey of more than 3 million low-income families in sixty-seven locations, sixty of them urban and seven rural. One disclosure was that, although only 8 percent of the families involved that were headed by white males had to allocate 35 percent or more of their total income for mortgage payments or for rent and utilities, 31 percent of the families headed by black women were in that unenviable predicament. And for that robust outlay they were in many instances dwelling in disagreeable accommodations.

The poverty problem, however, was not primarily a black problem. Relatively, yes: absolutely, no. For, percentages aside, there were nearly three times as many poor whites in America as there were poor blacks—17,500,000 to 7,700,000. (In 1960, there had been 11,500,000 such blacks, and they constituted 56 percent of the entire black population.) One big difference between these groups was that the white poor—for example, retired farmers too discouraged or disadvantaged to seek greener fields elsewhere— were in many instances scattered and old. The black poor were younger and were huddled together. One of every four poor whites was over sixty-five, so the membership of that inadvertent fraternity was likely to be fairly rapidly reduced by death; but only one of every ten poor blacks was in that older age group. Half of all the blacks in poverty were under eighteen, and they would be around for quite some time to come.

The black poor, by and large, were poorer than the white poor. On average, their 1970 income was $1,600 below the poverty line; the whites fell short of the mark by $1,300. It would have taken $11,400,000,000 a year to get the lot of them up to the point of marginal subsistence. The prospects of their some- how doing this on their own are dim. There is a direct correlation, as we shall see, between education and income. Nearly three quarters of the heads of poverty families never finished high school. One quarter of the heads of all poverty families had less than eight years of schooling. Only 2 percent of those families headed by college graduates were in poverty. There appears to be little correlation, however, between poverty and reluctance to work. Sixty-two percent of all male heads of poverty families and 43 percent of all female heads worked for a while in 1970; and 68 percent of the female heads who didn't work said that they couldn't because of their responsibilities at home. Of those male heads of these families who didn't work, 60 percent were over sixty-five, and 19 percent were ill or disabled.

What all Americans in poverty have in common is a knowledgeability that sets them dramatically apart from the poor in other countries. They are acutely and anguishedly aware how bum a deal they are getting compared to their fellow citizens. Unlike, say, an impoverished peasant in India or South America, the American poor, many of whom have cars, can travel around and see how well other people live. They can see it, indeed, without ever leaving their homes, for nearly all of them have television sets. They cannot readily be persuaded that poverty is a normal concomitant of American life.

As a result, they have aspirations and frustrations not widely shared by the needy any other place. But they can have few expectations of instant or even eventual amelioration of their lot. And just above them on the economic scale, hardly to be envied, are the near-poor, 10,200,000 strong in 1970, whom any little luckless turn of events could push down into the unqualifiedly poor group. The number of women-headed families in this near-poor category rose by a distressing 80 percent between 1959 and 1970. A lot of American women needed to be liberated in a very urgent way.

XVI

☆ ☆ ☆ ☆ ☆ ☆

Uncle Sam Slept Here

In 1970, there were 67,656,566 year-round housing units in the United States—that is, houses,
apartments, single rooms, and mobile homes. Apartments were looming larger and larger (literally as well
as statistically) on the American scene. While in the
1960s all housing units increased by 18 percent—a
not surprising increase, with a rise in population of 13
percent and the inevitable abandonment of out-
moded units—the increase in apartments was spectacularly larger: up by 36.8 percent nationally, up by
96 percent in the suburbs. Currently, for every two
apartment buildings rising in the central cities, one is
rising up just outside them. More than 5 million new
multi-unit residential structures went up in the decade. Their proliferation brought about one minus
figure in a country accustomed to pluses: sales of
electric washing machines went down. The reason
was that many of the new apartment buildings
offered communal laundry facilities as one of their
enticements—not to mention communal air-condi-

tioning, communal garbage disposal, and, all-important these days, collective security. (Thirty-six percent of all occupied units in the United States had some air-conditioning in 1970.) The trend toward apartment living is likely to accelerate in the years immediately ahead. By 1980, some 60 million Americans born since the Second World War will have grown up, and will be seeking homes of their own. A substantial number of them, by all indicators, will become apartment-dwellers.

For all that, we remain predominantly a nation of house-dwellers; despite the drift toward apartments, the homeowners among us rose in the sixties from 32,800,000 to 39 million. Seventeen million of all the housing units in the country—25 percent of the total—and 33 percent of all suburban units were built subsequent to 1960. In 1970, 63 percent of all American families owned a home. Among blacks as well as whites, home ownership increased, even in the South, where in 1960, 42 percent of the blacks owned a home of sorts, and where ten years later 47 percent did.

New one-family homes are now being sold at the rate of 596,000 a year, currently at a median price of about $33,700; in theory, it is sound economics for a family to pay a sum equal to twice its annual income for a home. (One of the anomalies revealed by the 1970 Census was that in the metropolitan areas of the nation there were 26,820 homes with a value of $50,000 or more that were inhabited by households with incomes under $2,000—23,346 of these instances involving single individuals of sixty-five or older. Strange existence.) Of all American families with incomes of $15,000 or more, 85 percent owned at least one home, and even half of those under $3,000 had a place that, whatever its deficiencies might be, they could accurately call their own. Generally, our houses were all at once getting larger and less crowded. In 1960, the average suburban family consisted of 3.5 people occupying 5.1 rooms. In 1970, there were only 3.3 of them and they had 5.3 rooms—a modest change, certainly, but one of significance when multiplied by more than 20 million.

Most demographers consider housing to be inadequate when there is more than one person to a room. The South suffers more than any other sector of the country from this particular affliction; in 10 percent of all its housing units in 1970, there were 1.01 or more persons to a room. But the South was at the same time most rapidly improving; in 1960, 16 percent of its units had been thus overcrowded. There were fewer and fewer cramped quarters in the central cities, furthermore, where one might have expected to find the most of them; in only 8.5 percent of all central-city residences were there more than a person to a room, and even among black central-city residences the rate was no more than 10 percent—a welcome reduction from the 20 percent rate that had prevailed ten years before.

Inasmuch as half of all the nation's housing now in use has been built since the Second World War, and few residences of any sort are now constructed without bathrooms, there have been remarkable advancements in the nation's plumbing, on which the Census Bureau has kept a watchful eye just about ever since the invention of the bathtub. (In 1930, the Bureau reminds us, nine of every ten farm homes not only had no indoor toilet but didn't have electricity, either.) The Bureau considers the plumbing inadequate in any residence that is missing its own flush toilet and either a shower or a tub. In 1970, there remained in the country 4,687,000 housing units that lacked them—6.9 percent of the total—but there had been steady progress. In 1960, 16.8 percent of the total had had unsatisfactory plumbing, and in 1950, 35.4 percent. Twenty years after that, 27.3 percent of all housing units not only had one bathroom but at least two. As Mississippi, with a 30 percent bad-plumbing rate, once again led (or trailed) all the states, so was California, where so many people had moved into so many new homes, the most hygienic state, with a rate of less than 8 percent.

Our houses have grown smaller than our grandparents' for a variety of reasons—escalating building costs, the scarcity of servants, the tendency of more and more people to spend more and more time away from home. Still another reason is a simple one: Households have been getting smaller. The national average dropped from 3.67 persons in 1940 to 3.3 in 1960 and 3.06 in the spring of 1972. There were 5,786,363 Americans living, in 1970, not in households of any sort but in group quarters—among them, 323,154 in nursing homes, 424,091 in mental hospitals, 927,514 in homes for the aged, and perhaps as many as half a million in communes and other informal arrangements. For students of the effects of transcontinental jet lag, it should perhaps be noted that California had more people than New York in old-age homes, but New York had more in mental institutions.

Almost one fifth of all housing units in 1972 were occupied by a solitary person. In March of that year, 12,200,000 Americans were living alone, and there were 57 percent more of their kind than there had been in 1960. Some of the new breed of loners were young men and women who had elected to leave the family nest nearly as soon as they could fly; between 1962 and 1972, the number of individuals under thirty-five who were living by themselves went up from 765,000 to 1,973,000. Many more were elderly widows or widowers who had elected to leave their married children, and in some instances had doubtless been ejected by them, for lack of space or lack of compatibility. In 1972, 28 percent of all persons sixty-five or over lived alone, as contrasted with 19 percent of them in 1962. Since so many of them had migrated to Florida, it followed logically that Florida—at 39.2 percent—had the lowest proportion among states of those housing units with three or more bedrooms. Delaware—with 60.8 percent—had the highest, many of its spare chambers no doubt being reserved for guests of duPonts.

In the whole South, during the 1960s, the number of elderly loners increased by 71.9 percent. They were apt to be enjoying, or at any rate experiencing, a longer period than any of their prototypes of what insurance men call survivorship—that period between the maturity of someone's children and the parent's death. When one added to this group those Americans in *two*-person households—perhaps a pair of grandparents, or a younger childless couple, or a brace of airline stewardesses—one arrived at the sizable total of 50 million people. Over half of *them* were married couples who had no children under eighteen living with them, and whose numbers increased between 1967 and 1971 from 13 million to 13,800,000. In North Dakota, 90 percent of all children under eighteen were living with both their parents; in Washington, D.C., 59.3 percent. Both areas were conforming to a national statistical pattern: North Dakota is unusually white and Washington unusually black; the percentage of all whites under eighteen living with both parents was 87.9, and of all blacks 54.

Many of the survivors were not actually old at all by contemporary standards, being perhaps in their early fifties, still employed, and, with no resident families to fret about day in and out, able to indulge themselves rather freely. Two million American households—4.6 percent of the total—had second homes in 1970, and a majority of these belonged to one- and two-person households. One fifth were owned by people over sixty-five. (There were 26,000 families or individuals with more than two homes.) Second homes were constructed at the rate of 20,000 a year in the 1940s, and 55,000 a year in the sixties. They would probably have multiplied even faster had it not been for the emergence of mobile homes and trailers, which today serve hundreds of thousands of families as a second home and even more as a principal residence.

There are 23,000 trailer parks in America accommodating 7 million persons. Mobile homes, which have to be towed, are being manufactured today at the rate of about 600,000 a year, and motor homes, which have built-in locomotive power, at a 100,000-a-year rate. Mobile homes multiplied by 170 percent between 1962 and 1972. In 1970, more than 2 million American households were occupying them—nearly half of these people in the South. Florida alone contained 171,469 of them, almost as many as California, more than twice as many as New York. Mobile homes were not only a warm-weather institution but a predominantly white one; only 4 percent of all of them anywhere were lived in by nonwhites. Almost one fifth of all mobile-home *owners* were sixty-five or older; one third of all the *renters* of them (321,417 households were living in rented mobile homes, and paying a median monthly rental of $97 for the dubious privilege) were under twenty-five. Because of their popularity, the rate of increase of single-family *non*-mobile home construction has ever since 1946 lagged behind the rate of increase of the population. In 1960, 7 percent of all new single-family units were mobile homes; in 1969, 29 percent; in 1970, 34 percent. Mobile homes now constitute 67 percent of all single-family units costing less than $25,000, 79 percent of those under $20,000, and 94 percent—so high are the price tags these days for conventional lares and penates—of those under $15,000.

The total number of mobile homes in use in 1971 was 2,072,887, and they represented 3.1 percent of *all* the country's housing. In Nevada, one of every twelve households occupied a mobile home. In the South, their number soared from 239,000 in 1962 to 868,000 in 1972; one third of the population of Manatee County, Florida, dwelt in them. They were further occupied by 13 percent of all families with the husband and wife both younger than twenty-five, a group that by contrast filled only 2 percent of all owner-occupied housing units. This statistic did not even include those sometimes even younger folk who camped out more or less permanently in old station wagons or panel trucks, occasionally with some of their parents' best bedding to keep them warm.

One tenth of the American population of sixty-five or older now lives in mobile homes, and it is accordingly not surprising that their settlements are glaringly visible in states like Arizona, where some of the elderly gravitate, and Iowa and South Dakota, where others rusticate. South Dakota scored a 50 percent increase in mobile homes in the 1960s; the biggest gainer on the New York Stock Exchange in 1971 was an Iowa company that manufactured them.

President Nixon declared in 1971 that the United States, to meet the demands that would arise for housing, would have to construct 2,500,000 new units in each of the following ten years. Mobile homes were already being turned out at a rate equivalent to more than one fifth of this American goal. Where they will all finally come to roost is hard to say. Certain things are known, though, about their pattern of peregrination. Most of them are moved only once every two and a half years, and some never budge at all from their point of purchase. So it can perhaps be safely said that America is becoming a land whose inhabitants are increasingly concluding that there is no nicer way to live than in an immobile mobile.

XVII

☆ ☆ ☆ ☆ ☆

The Junior Citizens

THE CENSUS BUREAU DEFINES "YOUTH" AS THAT
segment of the population between fourteen and
twenty-four. Between 1890 and 1960, this age group
increased in number at a fairly level rate, getting
bigger each decade by about 10 percent. At the end
of that seventy-year span, it had 12,500,000 more
members than it had had at the start of it, with
27,136,000 individuals fitting the definition in 1960.
In the single decade that followed, because so many
children had been conceived after the Second World
War, the youth contingent grew by 52 percent and
13,800,000—a greater increase in a single decade
than in all the previous seven decades together. In
1970, accordingly, there were 40,285,000 Americans
who qualified as youths. They comprised one fifth of
the nation. There were so many of them that between
1960 and 1970 the median age of the entire population of the United States fell from 29.5 to 27.9.

Contemporary American youth has a good many
unarguable attributes—no other age group can claim

so high a death rate in Vietnam—and it has been invested with some others that it may not deserve. Of the 68,864 known active drug addicts on the scene in 1970, for instance, only 5,714 were under twenty-one. It is widely believed, furthermore, that young people are indolent, parasitical, and ungrateful for the educational opportunities offered to them; and that, still further, they manifest their hostility toward establishmentarian values by refusing to do one specific thing that the establishment has traditionally prescribed for them: to go to school.

The figures do not appear to bear this out. The young men and women we see drifting around us, seemingly at loose ends, cannot be unreal, but statistically they are all but irrelevant. Perhaps we have been thinking of them as the tip of an iceberg when in fact they have been the whole berg. In any event, in terms of school enrollment, the 1960s were characterized more by continuity than by change, and indeed what change there was favored the establishment. In 1967, only 22 percent of sixteen- to twenty-four-year-olds were enrolled in some kind of educational institution; but by 1971, 31 percent were. The school dropout rate in 1970, for persons thirty to thirty-four—those who had for the most part finished their education ten years earlier—was 24 percent for whites and 41 percent for blacks. On the other hand, the rate for persons twenty to twenty-four—those who were just then finishing up—was only 16 percent for whites and 31 percent for blacks.

All told, in 1970, there were 1,600,000 males

between sixteen and twenty-one who were counted as school dropouts (1,300,000 whites, 344,670 blacks, 138,653 Spanish-heritages), but still there were 200,000 *fewer* dropouts than there had been in 1965. At the same time, the percentage of all Americans who completed high school was climbing. Between 1962 and 1972, it rose from 46.3 to 55.2 percent. And for selected younger people, like those between twenty and twenty-nine, the comparison was even more impressive: 65 percent of everybody in that bracket in 1960 had gone through high school, and 79.5 percent of the same group in 1971.

We probably think of dropping out as an aspect of contemporary urban life. Again, the figures interpose a caveat. There was a higher percentage of school dropouts in 1970 in the rural nonfarm areas of the country than in the cities. (More expectedly, there was also a higher percentage in the central cities of the metropolitan areas than in their suburbs.) On a national basis, the percentage of sixteen- and seventeen-year-olds *in* high school went up just about 100 percent in sixty years. In 1910, only 43.1 percent of that group was enrolled in school; by 1970, the figure was 89.3 percent.

Whatever young people's motivation might have been, at the end of the sixties, for staying in school, they had clearly not turned *en bloc* against organized education. During the decade, the number of fourteen- to seventeen-year-olds in school rose from 90 to 94 percent. These were the percentages *enrolled*. It is common knowledge that school *attendance*, particularly in the central cities, often falls considerably short these days of its potential. So there was doubtless a discrepancy between the number of individuals credited to the educational process and the number actually getting an education.

Notwithstanding, the Census Bureau's findings encouraged those Americans searching for intimations that young people had not overwhelmingly rejected their parents' society. In the fourteen- to twenty-four-year group, 97 percent of the males were either attending some kind of school or holding a job, and 98 percent of the females were either in school, or working, or keeping house. Thus, statistically, all but a handful of them were engaged in what is usually regarded as purposeful activity.

Of the approximately 48 million employed males of sixteen or older in the American labor force in 1970, 8 million were between sixteen and twenty-four. When one examines the number of them in each of the ten major occupational categories, one finds that the pattern of their employment is fairly consistent with that of all men, regardless of age. True, a slightly smaller percentage of the younger group had professional or technical jobs, and a considerably smaller percentage of them had managerial ones, but this was probably more attributable to plain youthfulness and inexperience than to any other factor. But in a number of classifications the young men seemed to be keeping pretty much in step with their fathers. The sixteen- to twenty-four-year-old workers were one sixth of all workers; they were one fourth of the clerical and service workers, one fifth of the operatives, one sixth of the salesworkers. There were 5.8 percent of all employed males who had elected, or been obliged, to become transport operatives; 5.5 percent of the younger men had, too. Of the entire work force 6.9 percent were in sales, as were 7 percent of the younger contingent. There were larger variations in some of the other categories, but none of such dimensions as to indicate that anything revolutionary had happened to the American configuration of labor.

The hope that a diploma might lead to a job had certainly kept a good many individuals in school who would otherwise have, in their vernacular, split. Two thirds of the female high-school graduates of 1970 soon afterward got white-collar jobs, a goal that was reached by only one third of their peers who failed to finish up. Quite a few of the young women who dropped out did so because of marriage, or motherhood, or both; whereas only 18 percent of the high-school graduates were married, 42 percent of the dropouts were.

Inasmuch as census-takers are persistently inquisitive about education and income, the Bureau has a lot of data on both, and in correlations of the two categories it usually turns out that, the more people have had of the former, the more they have got of the latter. If one accepts the proposition that a white-collar job is more congenial and more rewarding for either sex than a blue-collar job, then one need merely note that, while 12 percent of American males who dropped out of high school in 1970 ended up in the white-collar world, 95 percent of those who finished college joined that ostensibly privileged class.

To look at it another way, most of the money that is paid out for work in America goes to men between twenty-five and sixty-four. One third of these who, in 1971, were not high-school graduates were getting less than $6,000 a year; but only 13 percent of those with diplomas were doing that poorly. And, conversely, while 43 percent of those who, before 1971, had gone all the way through college were getting *more* than $15,000, only 22 percent of high-school graduates were doing as well, and a mere 6 percent of those who hadn't made it through the twelfth grade.

The average 1971 earnings for heads of families with a college degree was $15,530; for those who'd finished high school, $11,269; for those who'd stopped after elementary school, $7,668. The last time the Census Bureau computed the probable average lifetime earnings for males with four years of college, it came up with the figure of $586,047; those with less than eight years of primary and secondary school could look forward to no more than $214,000. Finally, according to the Bureau's learned projections, even the better educated among us must expect to have to do some scrambling for any kind of earnings; between 1970 and 1980, if prognostications hold up, there will be 9,800,000 additional university graduates added to the national labor force, but only 9,600,000 jobs available to all of them.

The high-school dropout rate for blacks was more than twice that of whites in 1970; among nineteen-year-olds, the respective rates for the races were 44 percent and 13 percent. The higher rate for the blacks might, among other things, have reflected their instinctive awareness, whether or not they were familiar with the statistics, that in *their* case the chances of employment were not drastically affected by academic credentials; the unemployment rate for black high-school graduates in 1970 was 15.8 percent, and for black dropouts of the same age an only marginally greater 18.1 percent. Given this discouraging state of affairs; given, moreover, the harsh reality that within the last few years it had become as increasingly difficult for *all* Americans of student age to get part-time jobs as for many Americans to get any kind; and given, finally, the supposed antipathy of much of American youth to the national work ethic, one might have surmised that there had been a marked falling-off among young people who contributed by their own labor to the cost of their education.

But that was not the case. There were *more* young Americans, not fewer, working their way through school in 1970 than there had been ten years earlier. Nearly 40 percent of all sixteen- to twenty-one-year-olds in high school or college were in the labor force—were, in other words, working or looking for work—at the end of the decade, as opposed to barely over 30 percent at the start of it. Moreover, 34.7 percent of these latter-day students had actually found some employment, compared with 20 percent of their predecessors. And the number of full-time college students in the labor force had gone up from 27 percent to 36.6 percent. For some of them, because of escalating tuitions and limited scholarship funds, it was plainly a choice of working, however distasteful that concept might be, or forgoing their education. And economic necessity no doubt was a factor in the determination of so many students to look for summer jobs: Of 12 million individuals between sixteen and twenty-one who were in school at the end of the 1960s, all but 2,500,000 either had a summer job or had tried to find one.

One should perhaps cautiously approach all statistics relating to the presence of young people in the labor force, for they wander in and out of it in a manner confusing to meticulous record-keepers, often working long enough merely to earn enough money to fulfill their short-term needs. But work they did, as hard as or harder than the youth of bygone, pre-counterculture days. And they earned considerably more than enough to cover their schoolbooks and lab fees: In one recent, four-year stretch, annual sales of phonograph records zoomed from $180,200,000 to $276,400,000.

Although many reservations have been expressed lately about the nature of American education, we are at least going through the motions of absorbing a lot of it. Among the findings of the 1970 Census was the benchmark news that for the first time in the nation's decennial stock-takings, more than half of its living adult citizens had graduated from high school. As recently as 1940, only 4.6 percent of all Americans twenty-five and older had finished college, and 60.4 percent of them had stopped their education after elementary school. In thirty years, there had been a drastic reversal; by 1970, 11 percent of the over-twenty-fives were college graduates, and only 26.6 percent of them had not got beyond the elementary level.

As for the *school-age* population, by 1970, 80 percent of *it* was graduating from high school. Here, the progress of American blacks had been especially noteworthy. In 1940, only 12 percent of them between twenty-five and twenty-nine had completed high school, and in 1950, only 23 percent. By 1970, more than 66 percent had. (Even 22.8 percent of rural blacks had.) To be sure, they were still markedly behind their white compatriots, but this was another gap that was narrowing. In the larger metropolitan areas of the country, where the percentage of whites over twenty-five with a high-school education or better had risen between 1967 and 1972 from 59.3 to 64.2 percent, that for blacks had gone from 38.7 to 41 percent. And, while all blacks were behind all whites, blacks who were twenty and twenty-one in 1970 had a collective median of 12.4 years of schooling—a bit *more* than high school.

At that level, they were very close to the whites of their age, and they came close at the same time that all American men over twenty-five finally caught up with all similar American women and matched *their*

[295]

median of 12.1 years. (Utah, with a median of 12.5, ranked as our most-educated state; Kentucky, with 9.9, was our least.) The countrywide median had been 10.6 years in 1969, and 9.3 in 1950. In 1940, when it stood at 8.6, the majority of Americans hadn't finished high school. The non-finishers became a minority late in the 1960s. As of March 1972, furthermore, 45.3 percent of all American *blacks* between twenty-two and twenty-four had finished high school.

The *kind* of education that many of these blacks were getting was something else again. More than twice as many blacks as whites were two years or more behind their modal grades, and there were more black males in that unhappy fix than females. Despite prodigious school-attendance figures, it was suspected in 1970 that our schools harbored some 10 million children—an unspecified but assuredly high proportion of them black children in central-city schools—with grave reading problems. Without remedial action, they were almost bound to find their deficiencies increasingly disadvantageous as they grew older, inasmuch as there were fewer and fewer niches in the economy that they could readily hope to fill. At the end of the Second World War about one third of all available jobs could be handled by unskilled laborers. By 1970, there were only half as many such educationally undemanding openings.

Still, it was heartening to be able to worry about *degrees* of reading achievement. It was not so long ago that a substantial number of Americans suffered from a far more hobbling handicap, economically, psychologically, and socially: the burden of illiteracy. As 1970 was a signal year in positive educational achievement, so also was it the decennial year in which the total of American illiterates began to approach six digits. Their number came to 1,400,000, of whom 509,000 were black. One percent of all whites over forty-five were illiterate, but 10 percent of comparable blacks. Most of these, one could have guessed, were living in the South. Less than 1 percent of all Iowans suffered from that deprivation; more than 6 percent of all Louisianians were afflicted by it. The South also predominated when it came to those Americans who, though not illiterate, had had no formal education beyond the fourth grade; that region in 1972 had 1,375,000 males over twenty-five —514,000 of them black—whose schooling had been thus severely constricted (more such men, in fact, than the rest of the country altogether).

The illiteracy rate should decline sharply in the next decade or two, inasmuch as the greatest concentration of illiterates was to be found in 1970 among the oldest blacks: 17.2 percent of black males over sixty-five and 16.2 percent of the elderly black females. The dying-off of older black illiterates in the 1960s was the principal cause of the dwindling national total, and their disappearance also affected the statistical nature of the black population in entirety: At the start of the decade, 7.5 percent of all American blacks had been illiterate, and at the end of it, only 3.6 percent.

A notable victim of the residential shift to the suburbs was private education. In 1965, about 15 percent of all the nation's children were in private schools; by 1971, only 10 percent. The faltering economy was only one cause of the shrinkage. Another important one was that parochial schools had become physically separated from their potential pupils. Some people are inclined to think of private schools as elitist academies for the rich, often with WASPish overtones, but in fact 90 percent of all private-school children had for many years been those in parochial—mainly Catholic—institutions. Most of these schools were in central cities, where the once high representation of white Catholics had been superseded by an equally high concentration of black non-Catholics. And most black children, it went without saying, did not attend private schools—a mere 4 percent of them, as opposed to 13 percent of all white children. Here again, though, money was an equalizer. Among families with incomes of $15,000 or more, 20 percent of the white children went to private schools, and so did a not too dissimilar 16 percent of the black children. Numerically, however, this involved only 63,000 black children.

As we have already become a nation where not to finish high school is the exception far more than the rule, so within the next decade or two might we also become one a majority of whose inhabitants are college graduates. More than half of all the 1970 high-school graduates matriculated at some kind of college. A young man who a generation previous might have gone straight from school to a job as an auto mechanic was apt to spend two years at a technical college and emerge as an automotive service engineer. Not that, as mentioned earlier, we are in danger of a dearth of plain mechanics.

In the fall of 1970, 1,692,000 of the 6,300,000 college students in America (8,100,000 by the following fall) were in junior colleges, and they were quite different from the students in four-year academies. The two-year-college students were more likely to be male than the four-year-college ones, more likely to be attending only part-time (34 percent of them, compared to 12 percent of first- and second-year students in the four-year places), more likely to be married (nearly half of them being over twenty), more likely to live off campus (all but 5 percent of them), and more likely to come from families of modest means. Ninety-two percent of them were in colleges that were almost entirely supported by public funds. The two-year colleges were responsible practically all by themselves for the rise in college enrollments between 1966 and 1971—with 700,000 of the 800,000 increase in freshmen and sophomores credited to their ranks.

By the end of the 1960s, almost 60 percent of the sons and daughters of families with incomes over $15,000 were making it to college, but only 14 percent of those from families under $3,000. Because of the mounting tuition charges of private institutions, and the revocation of student draft deferments, there was soon a leveling off in college enrollments. The only appreciable gains had been made, thanks to talent searches and scholarship funds, among those who a generation ago hardly ever experienced any kind of higher education. It was no surprise that 60 percent of the eighteen- and nineteen-year-olds in white metropolitan families were in college; it was surprising that 50 percent of the comparable young blacks also were. This special latter group had far outdistanced blacks in general; across the country, *they* constituted only about 9 percent of the college population. Still, that was a better showing than they made in most measurable facets of our society; and it might have been a hopeful augury that, while in 1972 the percentage of whites between eighteen and twenty-four on college campuses remained about the same as it had been five years before, the total black college enrollment of 727,000 represented an increase for blacks of a robust 211 percent in eight years.

In a single generation, the higher-education picture had changed radically, and not merely for blacks. Three quarters of the blacks in college came from families in which the head of the house was not college educated; but then so did three fifths of the whites. (Nearly a third of all living male college graduates have fathers who never went to high school.) A million students a year leave colleges now before they graduate; notwithstanding, in 1970, 16.2 percent of all Americans between twenty-five and twenty-nine had college degrees; by 1980, that figure might be up to 24 percent, and by 1990 to 30 percent.

One need only compare the experience of veterans

of our last three wars (Mississippi had the fewest, proportionately, of *them*) to get a notion of how much more thoroughly educated a nation we have become. Of those veterans availing themselves of the opportunities for further study offered under the G.I. Bill of Rights, 55 percent of the Second World War group had completed four years of high school. In the case of the Korean War, it was 71 percent, and of the Vietnam War, 92 percent. By the time the next war rolls along, the men expected to take part in it may be sufficiently well educated not to let it occur.

XVIII

☆ ☆ ☆ ☆ ☆

The Senior Citizens

O NE OF THE BIG CHANGES IN AMERICAN SOCIETY in the twentieth century has been the emergence of a sizable, influential, and ever more voluble group of older people—those so often designated "senior citizens" by their juniors. However spry any individual may seem or feel when he reaches sixty-five, that is the age at which, willy-nilly, he is consigned by the Census Bureau to the irreversible status of seniority. In 1900, when the life expectancy at birth of all Americans was forty-seven, there were merely 3 million of them who had reached the sixty-five-year watershed, and they comprised slightly less than 4 percent of the total population. By 1970, life expectancy had climbed to seventy, and there were alive (and not infrequently kicking) more than 20 million of the sixty-five-year-olds—virtually 10 percent of the nation.

In sheer bulk, they now form a significant portion of the body politic. They outnumber the total population of the twenty smallest states of the Union, and, because as we have seen they take their political responsibilities more seriously than do most younger people, candidates for elective office must take *them* seriously. Much of George Wallace's success was surely attributable to his assiduous courting of their support and his awareness of their frustrations. For they have many. Their biggest worry is their money, or their relative lack of it. The 1970 median income for the heads of all American families was $9,867; for the heads of all families who were sixty-five or over, it was $5,053. True, they had by and large smaller families and fewer dependents, but many of them fell far short of making ends meet. Social Security notwithstanding, in 1969 27.1 percent of all of them lived below the poverty line, and even after Social Security payments were slightly increased that year, the percentage fell merely to 22 percent.

Of the older folk not living with their families, 48.5 percent were living below the poverty level in 1970, and those in the farm regions were worse off than that. In the North Central states, only 5.2 percent of the entire population needed such assistance, but 38.3 percent of the over-sixty-fives did. In Arkansas, it was 48.8 percent. That many of them have found conservative politicians appealing may have stemmed less from any hardening of arteries or attitudes, or from a distaste for long hair, than from an understandable anxiety to conserve the purchasing power of the often fixed assets on which they rely to survive.

As the ranks of the over-sixty-fives have swelled, the size of American households has nonetheless noticeably diminished. The average number of individuals per household dropped from 3.37 in 1950 to 3.14 in 1970. Nowadays, practically nobody lives in the great majority of American homes except parents and their younger children. In 1950, more than 20 percent of all the older people were living with relatives, in most instances with their own grown children. But in twenty years this figure fell to 12.5 percent. The number of older men living in households of which they were not the head fell from 11 percent in 1961 to 7 in 1971, and of older women from 22 to 15 percent. The old folks have, as some students of geriatrics delicately put it, become ever more emphatically disengaged.

But this should not be interpreted to mean that they have necessarily been rejected by their children and grandchildren. For all the movement of older people to sun cities and mobile-home parks, for all the comparative independence that has lately characterized their existence, they are not especially isolated from their families. And indeed fewer of them make *permanent* moves than one might suspect. It is true that, like migratory geese, 1 million elderly Americans flock to the South every fall and flock back in the spring. But in 1971, only 1.4 percent of the group changed their residence from one state to another, and 84 percent of them still lived less than a mile away from at least one of their offspring, at least one of whom they visited at least once a week. Many American parents in their forties and fifties now see a good deal less of *theirs.*

There are all sorts of reasons for the residential separation of the older people from their blood relatives. For one thing, the extended-family concept has never—except to some degree in the case of blacks—figured importantly in the American way of life. For another, with the advent (in the 1920s and 1930s) of pension plans and (in 1936) of Social Security, quite a few older people now have resources to draw on, however skimpy, other than their savings and their children's benevolence. Anyone who turned sixty-five in the 1960s has known for most of his or her adult life that on all levels of government and many of private industry there were agencies and departments specifically set up to ameliorate the plight of the aged.

Not too long ago, there were hardly any, and most Americans used to continue working, because they had no alternative, until they died. Compulsory retirement at *any* age was far more often the exception than the rule. Men and women in their fifties had little hope of presiding over businesses or industries until somebody who outranked them died. Now, people advance in business faster (thus presumably more quickly acquiring larger means of later support) and at the same time are more quickly relieved of family burdens; by the time they reach fifty, their children are apt to be grown up and leading their own lives. The dimensions of the leisure class have been enormously broadened.

Whether or not most older people have cheerfully accepted their relatively isolated status is questionable. Not long ago, the Census Bureau began a series of long-range studies focused on people between fifty-eight and sixty-three—those on the brink of retirement and, in most cases, of partial or total separation from their families. The survey is being conducted on behalf of the Social Security Administration, which hopes to learn from it something about the emotional and psychological effects on older people of their changing lot.

If, for instance, they continue to live with their children, as a considerable number of them of course still do, are they better or worse off than they would be if they were disengaged? Is it easy for men and women to adjust from running households to becoming hangers-on? Do extroverts thereby become transformed into introverts, and if they do what effect does this have on domestic tranquillity? And are the benefits of whatever security they derive from being taken care of by their children offset to any measurable degree by a dilution of their own self-importance?

Whatever the findings, it may not make much difference, for there simply is no longer a permanent place in most contemporary households for grandparents; as we have seen, new housing is not designed to accommodate them. It is hard to tuck somebody off into an extra room if that extra room does not exist.

As the older population has grown, its makeup has altered. In 1930, there were more men over sixty-five than there were women; as of March 1971, the group was made up of 11,600,000 women and 8,500,000 men. In 1920, American women outlived their fellow men by just one year; in 1971, by seven years. In the over-sixty-five group there were only seventy-two men for every 100 women, and the projection was that by 1990 the ratio would be sixty-eight to 100. Inactivity is sometimes thought to be a leading factor in the death of older males, and the American experience would seem to bear this out: In 1900, two thirds of the males over sixty-five continued to work; in 1971, only 26 percent of all males over sixty-five. In 1950, when pensions and retirement plans were less prevalent, it had been 46 percent. The incidence of continuing toil has been high, as previously noted, in South Dakota, where farmers' sons have fled the coop and their fathers are obliged to keep on cleaning it; and in Utah (30.3 percent), where the work ethic is strongly cherished. But in nearby Arizona, where the incidence of basking in the sun is high, only 19.1 percent of these elderly stayed in the labor force, and in Florida, unless one counts gin rummy as work, only 17.5 percent.

One reason for the prominence in the one-person-household category of individuals over sixty-five is that there are so many elderly widows around. Most people do not prefer to live alone, and a two-person household is not merely more congenial, as a rule, than solitude, but is also a good deal more economical. The image of our older people as forlorn, abandoned, and condemned to live out their days in nursing homes or hospitals is, incidentally, a false one; only one of every twenty-five Americans over sixty-five is to be found in any kind of institution.

Accordingly, in an era when fewer and fewer of the younger, conventionally marriageable Americans are actually getting married, there has been a jump in marriages among the old. More than 35,000 marriages now occur annually in which at least one of the participants is over sixty-five. There would probably be even more of them than there are were it not that for every widower that old there are now four widows. And, alas for the widows, while twice as many of these older men are married as of the women, the widowers do not always seek out their contemporaries for wives. (Quite a few of these widows have a special attractiveness; of the 60,000 Americans estimated to have a net worth of more than a million dollars, one sixth are women over sixty-five.) There are 3,000 American husbands today who are over seventy-five and have wives under twenty-five; a mere 2,000 women over fifty-five have husbands under twenty-five.

Most Americans die in December and January, a chilling statistic that all by itself would justify a mass migration of the old to regions with year-round warm weather. But far fewer of them can afford to make such a move than would probably like to. Of the states that have recently had the highest percentages of over-sixty-fives, nearly all have notably nasty winters—Iowa, Kansas, Maine, Massachusetts, Missouri, Nebraska, South Dakota, and Vermont. Until 1966 Iowa led the nation; 12.5 percent of its population was over sixty-five. Now Florida, one of the few states in which large-print newspapers can profitably be published, has taken the lead, with 14.6 percent. (Alaska is the coldest state and, appropriately, has the fewest over-sixty-fives—just 3 percent of them.) The over-sixty-five population of Florida actually doubled in the 1960s, going from 553,000 to 1,090,000 (most of these newcomers from the Northeast), but even so the picture of that state as a haven of senility is grossly overdrawn: Among all the country's Standard Metropolitan Statistical Areas, the one with the highest concentration of older people in 1970 was the Tampa–St. Petersburg area. Yet even there they came to merely 30.7 percent of the resident population. That was enough, however, to give St. Petersburg one statistical distinction. In most American communities, annual births comfortably exceed annual deaths. In St. Petersburg, in 1968, there were almost twice as many deaths as births.

The American *counties* that in 1970 had a 15 percent or greater representation of over-sixty-fives were the backwater ones in which elderly people remained—in many instances probably entrapped—as their children and grandchildren drifted away toward the cities, those counties in the main that achieved their population crests at the turn of the century and have been ebbing ever since. These counties extended south in a broad belt from Minnesota down toward the Gulf of Mexico. There were twenty-one of them in Kansas alone, and thirty-five in Texas. Like the older people so evident within their boundaries, they were dying.

The stagnant counties are predominantly white. There are still plenty of older black men and women sitting on the run-down porches of Southern farmhouses, but half of all the blacks over sixty-five now live in central cities. The white people sitting on tenement-house stoops not far away are in large part poor elderly whites. In the 1960s, as the white exodus to the suburbs came to full flower, the overall white population of the central cities hardly changed at all, but the over-sixty-five central-city white population resisted the trend (it could not afford to participate in it) and *increased* concurrently by 8 percent. The upshot was that one of every seven whites remaining in a central city in 1970 was over sixty-five. Of those Americans who were both elderly and poor, incidentally, the white poor were older: Persons over sixty-five comprised 17 percent of all low-income whites in 1970, but only 7 percent of all low-income blacks. The whites got poorer as they left their good earning years behind them; among blacks, poverty was not selective but pervasive.

The worst-off Americans in 1970 were the loneliest. Forty-nine percent of all of us of any race who lived alone also lived below the poverty level—a sobering fact at a time when longevity was increasing. And the outlook is not especially more promising for all older couples, many of whom, it would seem, have precious little to comfort them except each other. At last report, more than half of all married couples in the over-sixty-five bracket had to make do on less than $3,000 a year. To offset the fortunate 7 percent of them who had incomes of more than $10,000, there was another 7 percent who had to get by somehow on less than $1,000. The poor got poorer, the rich got richer still, and the old, for so many of whom Sun City was about as realistically attainable as Heaven, merely got older. Their numbers are growing today at a rate greater than that of the rest of the population—a 21 percent annual increase as against 13 percent. There are about 350,000 more of them among us every year, and we can predict with fair accuracy how many of them will be around by the year 2000, inasmuch as the vagaries of fertility cannot affect *them;* anybody who is going to be sixty-five by the end of the century has already got to be alive.

By then, there should be some 29 million of them. And, as the American life span is prolonged, there will be even more individuals around who are the oldest of the old. In 1900, only 29 percent of all our people over sixty-five had reached seventy-five. By 1970, 38 percent of the elderly were over seventy-five, and by 2000, in all likelihood, it will be 43 percent. The Census Bureau population experts who deal in projections have come up with some beguiling hypotheses about the possible composition of the United States at the start of the twenty-first century. If, as seems not improbable, Zero Population Growth has become a *fait accompli* for America, and if—a less credible contingency—immigration no longer contributes to the total, the total population in 2000 would be only (only!) 251,056,000.

There would be some interesting changes in the makeup of the country. Whereas in 1970 it contained 17,154,337 individuals less than five years old and 7,630,046 over seventy-five, in 2000 it would have just about the same number of pre-schoolers—18,147,000—but half again as many of the pre-octogenarians—12,429,000 people over seventy-five. (Among them would be 7,927,000 women and 4,501,000 men.) After the population leveled off so that births and deaths were in balance, 7 percent of the total would be people over seventy-five, and the median age for the entire nation would be 37.2 years—a median considerably in excess of the life expectancy of some of the less developed nations on earth. There would be so many Americans around over thirty that the under-thirty group might even start listening to them again.

XIX

☆ ☆ ☆ ☆ ☆ ☆

Summing Up

W<small>HAT</small> <small>DO WE SEE, AS WE LOOK AT THE</small> U<small>NITED</small> States as a whole, two thirds of its way through the twentieth century and on the verge of entering its own third century as an independent nation?

We see a country in which the longstanding national bent for restlessness is still apparent—with one fifth of its inhabitants changing their residences in every year—but in which, at the same time, the national bent for exploring new frontiers has all but disappeared: Most of the turbulent movement is within or toward already settled regions, and specifically to metropolitan areas, in which three fourths of the population—150 million people—have themselves firmly, if not always contentedly, planted. They are there because what jobs there are are there, and until new industries are established elsewhere, new towns will not amount to much.

We see, though, an increasing lack of interest in *city* living. The suburbs, concluding a long challenge to our central cities as residential magnets, have finally emerged triumphant. Our cities, north, south, east, and west, are shrinking. They are also getting blacker, as blacks remain in them (though they are no longer pouring into them) while middle-class whites drift toward their fringes. As a result, the fringes are becoming more and more urbanized.

We see that migration to the West Coast, and especially to California, has markedly diminished, and that there is a new pattern of migration, toward the South, concentrated for the present in Florida. The central portion of the nation has, by comparison with its coastal areas, been relatively stagnant. But who can say that the inescapable demand for breathing space will not soon bring about still another migratory pattern, this time back to the plains and farms whence so many once traditional residents have fled?

The returning sons and daughters, however, will only rarely elect to till the soil. Our nation has become one in which fewer and fewer people are working with their hands in any sphere of activity: Among the most memorable revelations of the 1970 Census was that there were in America more white-collar workers than blue-collar ones, and more men engaged in services of one sort or another than in the manufacturing that used to be our hallmark of enterprise.

Everybody is getting richer, we perceive, though of course it doesn't mean much as the value of the dollar is constantly being whittled down. Still, we have also got to the historic point where the median income for all Americans, prosperous and impoverished alike, is above the $10,000 mark. Withal, there remain some 25 million of us who live below our officially designated poverty level, a dismal state of affairs in a country whose economy has finally reached the trillion-dollar level.

We see that the women of our country, who by their breeding habits chiefly determine the size of its population, have spontaneously and all but unanimously decided—for the time being at least—to keep our numbers from escalating out of sight, and that as the 1970s got under way they had reached the stage of producing children at a lower rate, never before achieved, than that required merely to sustain the population at its present level.

So there will be fewer young people in the years immediately ahead; and "youth" will probably be less of a preoccupation to the rest of the country than it was in the heady 1960s. In a way that may be too bad; the country may end up considerably duller.

As women are having fewer children, moreover, they are becoming an increasingly significant factor in our labor force. More of them are working than ever before, but they are still the victims of shameful sexist discrimination. They have a long way to go—and in this respect they have not yet been able to exercise much influence—before they attain economic parity with men.

Two out of every five *married* women now work, and only one of every twenty-five working women is in domestic service—almost precisely the same proportion as the percentage of women now to be found holding managerial positions.

A quick look at some of our other ratios: One of every hundred Americans now lives in California, our most populous state. One of every hundred never goes to school. Nearly one of every hundred is a black whom the 1970 Census failed, for one reason or another, to include in its final head count. One of every thousand Americans served in 1970 as a census-taker.

One of every five of us was born after the Second World War, and an identical 20 percent of us are living in a state other than the one they were born in. One of every 200 of us is illiterate, and one of every 200—the statistical similarity is coincidental—has newly moved to the South, our most populous *region,* within the last five years. Fewer than 5 percent of all the people in the country do not have a television set. Eighty percent of all of us now finish high school, and have access to at least one automobile.

As we peer hazily at the future, we can guess from the disclosures about our immediate past that among our most gainfully employed fellow residents—gainfully, it is to be hoped, not only for them but for all the rest of us—will be our urban and regional planners. For, if the trends now visible to us persist, urban living will be the lot of ever-growing numbers of our citizenry, and local governments will be under mounting pressure to cope with the urbanological problems that confront them. We had 9,053 urban and regional planners in our midst in 1970 (7,954 men, 1,099 women), and 5,818 of them were already in public administration—4,780 of these working for local governments.

So we already had close to 5,000 presumed experts wrestling on a local level with local concerns. It may be an ominous portent of things to come that, of these 1970 planners, 166 were employed by various welfare agencies.

Blacks are catching up so slowly with whites that they will probably continue for some time to come to receive a share of our welfare dollars disproportionate to their numbers. But in several areas—in education, in housing, and to a lesser degree in income—blacks have been progressing at a faster clip than ever before. They are still substantially behind whites in almost every measurable aspect of American life, but at least they have doubled their purchasing power, as a group, since the middle of the twentieth century. Those blacks who can afford it have already joined the whites in the suburbs, and as more blacks climb up the economic ladder the suburbs will get less white.

They will begin to get even more crowded, too, than they now are, and they will have to solve this problem either by extending their borders, as so many of our metropolitan areas have done in recent years, or by building more and more multi-family dwellings. The suburban apartment house (not to mention the mobile home) will be the residence of increasingly large numbers of people.

And the numbers—the temporary achievement of Zero Population Growth notwithstanding—will increase. We will probably have something like 270 million people in the United States by the start of the twenty-first century. And because immigration has now trickled off to 400,000 a year—only one newcomer for every 2,000 oldtime inhabitants—America will gradually become close to 100 percent American. In 1970, 83 percent of all our residents were native Americans whose parents were also native Americans. This percentage figure will increase year by year, until by the turn of the century probably nine tenths of the inhabitants of the United States will be indisputable indigenes. Whatever happens to us between now and then or after then, good or bad, we can hardly attribute any longer to foreign influences among us. We will have only ourselves to praise or blame.

Index

☆ ☆ ☆ ☆ ☆ ☆

Dropouts, 288–289
  black, 233, 288–289,
    293
  decrease in, 289
  high-school, 293
Drug addicts, 288
Dwight, Timothy, 186

E
East, the, 75
  migration to, 78
Eastern Airlines, 208
Ebony, 62
Eckler, A. Ross, 27
Economic Census, 23
  data for, 23–24
Economy, national
  birth rate and, 130
  census and, 163
  women and, 145–148
Education, 173, 288–301, 322
  blacks and, 98, 231–233,
    295–296
  college, 295, 298–299
  cost of, to state and local
    governments, 134–135
  and decline in population,
    134
  as factor in migration, 79–80
  income and, 291–292
  of Mexican-Americans,
    209–210
  private, 298
  public, 36
  and successful marriage,
    142–143
Elderly, the, 305–313 (*See also*
    Widowers; Widows)
  female, 309–310
  homes for, 279
  illiteracy among, 297
  income of, 313–314
  median, 306

  in labor force, 310
  living alone, 279–280, 313
  living in mobile homes, 282,
    307
  marriage among, 311
  migration of, 86–87, 307
    311
  number of, 305, 314–315
Elections, 1972, black vote in,
    112–113
Electric appliances, 239, 244
Electricity, 239, 278
Embalmers, 169, 172–173
Emigration, 177, 193–194
Employment (*See also* Jobs)
  of blacks, 234–236
  changes in type of, 153–156
  of children, 34
Energy consumption, 239–240
England, 243
  emigrants from, 183,
    187–188, 196
English language, 181
Europe
  emigrants from, 187–190,
    195–199
  Western, voting in, 15
Executives, salaries of, 163,
    166

F
Fairfield County, Connecticut,
    251
  compared with Tunica
    County, Mississippi,
    252–256
Farmers, 110, 155
Farm products, annual sales
  of, 102
Farms, 320 (*See also*
    Agriculture)
  abandoned, 70
  urban, 110

occupationally
consequential, 159
median age of, 154
salaries of (*see* Salaries)
and transportation, 247–
249
unskilled, 155–156, 296
white, ages of, 167
white-collar versus
blue-collar, 156–157,
199, 320
women (*see* Women,
working)
World War I, 81, 131, 194
World War II, 80, 131–132,
301
Wyoming, 5–6, 79, 99

Y

Youth
attributes of, 287–288
defined, 287
employed, 290–291
number of, in the United
States, 287, 321
parents and, 290
working while in
educational institutions,
293–294

Z

Zero Population Growth, 114,
125, 129–130, 135–136,
206, 314, 324
Zitter, Meyer, 128, 130